The
Stress Management
Program

INVENTORIES, ACTIVITIES
& EDUCATIONAL HANDOUTS

by John J. Liptak, Ed.D.

illustrated by Amy L. Brodsky, LISW

The Stress Management Program
Inventories, Activities and Educational Handouts

© 2005 by Wellness Reproductions & Publishing

International copyright protection is reserved under Universal Copyright Convention, and bilateral copyright relations of the U.S.A.

The original purchaser of this book is authorized to reproduce and use the individual items in this book for the generation of creative activity in a psychiatric/theraputic/education setting. However, this book may not be reprinted or resyndicated in whole or in part as a reproducible worksheet collection, or for any other purpose without written permission from the publisher.

This publication is sold with the understanding that the publisher is not engaged in rendering psychological, medical or other professional services.

Library of Congress Catalog Card Number: 2003116256
ISBN: 1-893277-35-6

WELLNESS REPRODUCTIONS & PUBLISHING
A Brand of Sunburst Visual Media

P.O. Box 9120 . Plainview, N.Y. . 803-9020
1.800.669.9208 • FAX 1.800.501.8120 • www.wellness-resources.com

DEDICATION

Any work of this type is a synergistic product of many minds, hearts, and souls.

This book is dedicated to some very special people in my life:

To my wife
Kathy
Who loves and supports me

To my mother and father
Betty and John
who always pushed me to do my best.

To two very special people in my life
Estelle Leutenberg & Kathy Khalsa
Who believed in me and this project and made
the publication of this book possible.

ACKNOWLEDGMENTS

A special thanks goes to Amy L. Brodsky for her fabulous illustrations included in this book. Amy's creativity and skills as an artist give this book a unique, user-friendly feel that adds to the impact of the assessments.

I would also like to thank all of the other people who have supported me, provided me with constructive feedback, kept me on task, and provided valuable ideas and suggestions in the completion of this project.

©2005 Wellness Reproductions & Publishing 1.800.669.9208

TABLE OF CONTENTS

(continued on reverse side)

©2005 Wellness Reproductions & Publishing 1.800.669.9208

TABLE of CONTENTS *(continued)*

©2005 Wellness Reproductions & Publishing 1.800.669.9208

INTRODUCTION

Stress is often defined as our reaction to any changes in our daily lives that require us to adjust or respond. Nobody is immune from stress because it is all around us – in our relationships with family members, in our relationships with friends, on our job, at school, in our communities, and in our world. It is ever-present in our lives and can be felt as we respond to environmental pressures, stimuli, and changes. Adaptation to different types of stress is a continuous process. People are able to deal effectively with many of these stressors, but too much can damage our relationships and our health. Thus, a little bit of stress in our lives is desirable and can even enhance our lives, but an overload of stress can affect our well-being.

Stress is caused by the body's natural instinct to protect itself. This instinct is good in emergencies, but if it goes on for too long in response to life's daily problems and changes, it can cause adverse physical and psychological symptoms.

A wellness approach suggests that each of us can learn to manage the negative effects of too much stress in our lives. Wellness is a holistic approach to stress management that focuses on our emotional, mental, spiritual, social, occupational, and physical well-being. Wellness is a lifestyle approach that is consciously directed toward maintaining a balance between ourselves and the stressors in our environment.

Therefore, we must learn to anticipate and monitor stress as much as we possibly can. We must begin to recognize the early warning signs of stress and try to maintain positive healthy ways of coping with change. Remember that all people react differently to stress and we all must learn about the tools and techniques that can help us to manage stress effectively.

ABOUT THIS BOOK

This book, *The Stress Management Program: Inventories, Activities, & Educational Handouts*, contains five separate modules of informal assessments and activities that will help your clients and students learn more about themselves and their effectiveness in managing stress. These modules serve as an avenue for individuals to engage in self-reflection, as well as in group experiences revolving around important topics. This book includes directions for easy assessment, scoring and interpretation. In addition, it contains group activities and educational handouts that can be used as overheads or turned into transparencies to assist the facilitators who use the assessments in group sessions or in workshops.

Everything in this book is completely reproducible and can be photocopied for client and student use.

THE ASSESSMENTS CONTAINED IN THIS BOOK:

- **Level of Stress Scale** helps individuals identify how much stress they are experiencing in their life and find ways to manage their stress.

- **Healthy Lifestyle Inventory** helps individuals identify the dimensions in their life in which they have a sense of wellness and those in which they do not.

- **Coping with Stress Scale** helps individuals to identify their style for coping with stress and change.

- **Resilient Personality Inventory** helps individuals identify how hardy they are in times of stress and change.

- **Time Management Scale** helps individuals identify strengths and weaknesses in how they managing their time and learn more effective methods of time management.

LAYOUT OF THE BOOK

The Stress Management Program: Inventories, Activities, & Educational Handouts is designed to be used either individually or as part of an integrated curriculum with adolescents or adults. You may choose to administer one of the assessments to a group with whom you are working, or you may choose to administer some of the assessments over one or more days.

THIS BOOK INCLUDES FIVE MODULES, EACH OF WHICH CONTAINS:

- **Assessment Instruments** — Five stress-management skills assessment inventories with scoring directions, interpretation materials and exploration activities, designed to be used independently or as part of a series of stress management activities conducted over several days. Group facilitators should choose one or more of the activities that are relevant to their clients or student population.

- **Group Activities** – Step-by-step group experiences for use by the group facilitator.

- **Pre- and Post-Tests** — Questions and answers for each of the five assessments are included for use as pre- and post-test indicators of participant growth.

- **Educational Handouts** — Four handouts per assessment for instructional use and personal insight work.

IN ADDITION, THIS BOOK CONTAINS:

- **Educational Social Skills Handouts** – Five general educational handouts on stress management that can be used in conjunction with any of the stress-management assessments or group experiences. These handouts can be converted into masters for overheads and/or transparencies.

- **Additional Resources** — References for other stress-management materials.

©2005 Wellness Reproductions & Publishing 1.800.669.9208

WHO SHOULD USE THIS PROGRAM?

This book has been designed as a practical tool for teachers, counselors, group leaders, therapists, life skills instructors and other helping professionals. Depending on the role of the professional using *The Stress Management Program: Inventories, Activities, & Educational Handouts* and the specific group's needs, these modules can be used individually or combined for a more comprehensive approach.

WHY USE INFORMAL ASSESSMENTS?

Informal assessments are important in teaching various stress-management skills because they:

- are a quick, nonthreatening way for people to learn about themselves.
- are based on general life-skills themes that allow for a comprehensive, holistic approach.
- can be tailored to each individual's specific life situation.
- can be used with an individual or in a group setting, such as counseling groups or classes.
- can be easily administered, scored and interpreted.

Because the assessments are presented in a straightforward and easy-to-use format, individuals can self-administer, score and interpret each assessment at their own pace.

EDUCATIONAL
STRESS-MANAGEMENT SKILLS HANDOUTS

The following handouts have been designed to accompany the modules included in this book. They can be used at the beginning of group sessions, to introduce different topics related to stress management, or to initiate group discussions about stress-management skills in general.

Good Stress Managers

Sources of Stress

Signs of Wellness

A Lifestyle Approach
to Stress Management

Wellness Dimensions

©2005 Wellness Reproductions & Publishing 1.800.669.9208

PEOPLE WHO MANAGE STRESS WILL

- [ ] interpret the stress in their life accurately.

- [ ] anticipate and regulate stressors as much as possible.

- [ ] believe they can influence events and their reactions to events.

- [ ] maintain healthy habits (sleeping regularly, eating nutritiously, exercising) to build resistance and prevent stress.

- [ ] recognize the warning signs of physical and mental stress.

- [ ] regulate their thinking about stressful events.

- [ ] use constructive, rather than destructive, reactions to stress.

- [ ] maintain an ongoing sense of meaning in their lives.

- [ ] develop and utilize a strong support system.

- [ ] contribute to the wellness of other people, communities and organization.

©2005 Wellness Reproductions & Publishing 1.800.669.9208

SOURCES OF STRESS

Stress in your life can come from a variety of sources including:

☐ Relationship problems

☐ Conflict between your goals and behaviors

☐ Self-imposed thoughts and behaviors like perfectionism and impatience

☐ Work overload

☐ Economic factors such as unemployment, poverty, and debt

☐ Threat of harm

☐ Increasing demands at home and in the workplace

☐ Divorce

☐ Noise and pollution

☐ Too many demands on your time

©2005 Wellness Reproductions & Publishing 1.800.669.9208

SIGNS OF WELLNESS

☐ Presence of a social-support network

☐ Increased sense of meaning and purpose

☐ Increased spiritual involvement

☐ Positive outlook on life

☐ Episodic peak experiences

☐ Kind sense of humor

☐ Supportive social relationships

☐ Interest in physical activity

☐ More energy

☐ Increased self-confidence

☐ Ability to adapt to change

☐ Increased creativity

©2005 Wellness Reproductions & Publishing 1.800.669.9208

A LIFESTYLE APPROACH TO STRESS MANAGEMENT

The effective stress-management approach includes many of the following factors:

☐ Taking personal responsibility for the effective management of stress in your life

☐ A holistic approach that integrates mind and body in minimizing and controlling stress

☐ Small, gradual changes that integrate stress-management tools and techniques over time

☐ Balanced lifestyle that combines work and play, self-interest and the well-being of others, stimulation, and contemplation

☐ Awareness of the stress in your life, what causes it, how it is harmful and how you can cope with stress

☐ An action-orientation in which you take an active role in identifying the stress in your life and coping with it

☐ Finding the stress-management tools and techniques that work for you

☐ Lifelong changes in your approach to other people, your body, your mind, your time, your work, and your play

©2005 Wellness Reproductions & Publishing 1.800.669.9208

LEVEL of STRESS MODULE

The Level of Stress Scale helps people identify how much stress they are experiencing in their lives and find ways to manage their stress.

INDEX

Answers to the pre- and post-test — page 2:	
1. All stress is bad	False
2. Stress cannot be eliminated, but can be controlled	True
3. Some stress can actually enhance performance	True
4. It is difficult to recognize the early warning signs of stress	False
5. Stress only affects adults	False

©2005 Wellness Reproductions & Publishing 1.800.669.9208

LEVEL of STRESS SCALE

PRE- and POST-TEST

NAME: _____ DATE: _____

The following true-or-false questions
are designed to determine your knowledge
of skills in detecting and managing stress.

Please circle Ⓣ if you think the statement is TRUE
and Ⓕ if you think the statement is FALSE.

---

1. All stress is bad . . . . T   F

2. Stress cannot be eliminated, but can be controlled . . . . T   F

3. Some stress can actually enhance performance . . . . T   F

4. It is difficult to recognize the early warning signs of stress . . . . T   F

5. Stress only affects adults . . . . T   F

©2005 Wellness Reproductions & Publishing 1.800.669.9208

LEVEL of STRESS SCALE

Name:

_____

_____

Gender:

_____

Date:

_____

Age:

_____

©2005 Wellness Reproductions & Publishing 1.800.669.9208

DIRECTIONS

A little bit of stress can be stimulating and can help you to reach states of peak performance, meet challenges, and excel in emergency situations. However, too much stress can hurt your emotional, physical, cognitive, and behavioral wellness. A certain amount of stress in your life cannot be avoided, but the management of stress in your life is a critical life skill. The Level of Stress Scale (LSS) was designed to help you explore how much stress you are experiencing in your life and to help you to identify how the stress is manifesting itself.

This assessment contains 32 statements that are related to the signs and symptoms of stress that you are currently exhibiting. Read each of the statements and decide whether or not the statement describes you. If the statement is truw, circle the number next to that item under the "true" column. If the statement is false, circle the number next to that item under the "false" column.

In the following example, the circled number under "false" indicates the statement is not true of the person completing the inventory.

	TRUE	FALSE
Little things rarely bother me	2	(1)

This is not a test. Since there are no right or wrong answers, do not spend too much time thinking about your answers. Be sure to respond to every statement.

Turn to the next page and begin.

©2005 Wellness Reproductions & Publishing 1.800.669.9208

LEVEL of STRESS SCALE

		TRUE	FALSE
(A)	Little things rarely bother me.	2	1
(A)	I often have difficulty making decisions.	1	2
(A)	I rarely get bored.	2	1
(A)	I don't care when plans change.	2	1
(A)	I am often thinking about other things and don't listen.	1	2
(A)	I am often unable to concentrate.	1	2
(A)	I rarely experience fuzzy, unclear thinking.	2	1
(A)	I find myself forgetting things lately.	1	2
(B)	I often have a strong urge to "run away from things."	1	2
(B)	I am excited to get up in the mornings.	2	1
(B)	I often have a strong urge to cry unexpectedly.	1	2
(B)	I rarely have emotional ups and downs.	2	1
(B)	I am rarely nervous about things in my life.	2	1
(B)	I am often fearful even when there is nothing to fear.	1	2
(B)	I rarely get depressed about anything.	2	1
(B)	I have been having feelings of hopelessness.	1	2

Turn to the next page and continue.

LEVEL of STRESS SCALE

		TRUE	FALSE
(C)	I rarely lash out at other people.	2	1
(C)	I often find myself talking faster than usual.	1	2
(C)	I like being around other people.	2	1
(C)	I often feel short-tempered.	1	2
(C)	I have been sleeping about eight hours a night.	2	1
(C)	I often catch myself verbally attacking others.	1	2
(C)	I do not act too quickly, but I think before acting.	2	1
(C)	I have withdrawn from people lately.	1	2
(D)	My appetite has remained the same.	2	1
(D)	I feel tired a lot of the time.	1	2
(D)	I rarely drink alcoholic beverages.	2	1
(D)	I have not experienced chest pain in the last six months.	2	1
(D)	I often have an upset stomach.	1	2
(D)	I feel nervous a lot of the time.	1	2
(D)	I find myself biting my fingernails a lot.	1	2
(D)	I often can feel my heart "racing."	1	2

Go to the scoring directions on the next page.

©2005 Wellness Reproductions & Publishing 1.800.669.9208

SCORING DIRECTIONS

The Level of Stress Scale (LSS) is designed to measure how much stress you are currently experiencing. To get your (A) Cognitive score, total the numbers you circled for statements marked (A), in the previous section. You will get a score from 8 to 16. Put that number on the line next to the (A) Cognitive Total scale that follows. Then, do the same for the other three scales: (B) Emotional Total, (C) Behavioral Total, and (D) Physical Total.

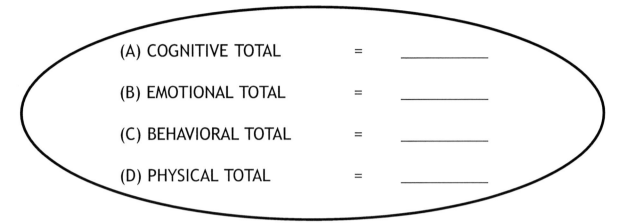

(A) COGNITIVE TOTAL   =   _____

(B) EMOTIONAL TOTAL   =   _____

(C) BEHAVIORAL TOTAL   =   _____

(D) PHYSICAL TOTAL   =   _____

Then add the four scores you listed above to get your Grand Stress Total. Total scores on this assessment range from 32 to 64. Put your Grand Total score in the space below:

GRAND STRESS TOTAL   =   _____

PROFILE INTERPRETATION

SCORES FROM 8 TO 10 IN ANY SINGLE AREA, OR A TOTAL FROM 32 TO 42, indicate that you are probably experiencing a great deal of stress in your life. A low score suggests that you are probably experiencing cognitive, emotional, behavioral, and / or physical stress that is preventing you from living your life effectively.

SCORES FROM 11 TO 13 IN ANY SINGLE AREA, OR A TOTAL SCORE FROM 43 TO 53, indicate that you are experiencing some stress in your life, but not an excessive amount. Your score is similar to other people taking the scale. It may suggest that you are experiencing stress in one or two of the areas, but that you are able to manage the stress fairly well.

SCORES FROM 14 TO 16 IN ANY SINGLE AREA, OR A TOTAL FROM 54 TO 64, indicate that you are not experiencing very much stress in your life. A high score suggests that you have been effective in managing your stress and that any stress you do have is not negatively affecting your daily life.

SCALE DESCRIPTIONS

SCALE A — COGNITIVE STRESSORS

People scoring low on this scale sometimes suffer from a lack of concentration, illogical thinking, confusion and lapses in memory. They are unable to think clearly or remember information well. This often results from having too many stressors in a short period of time. Cognitive distress can be related to the other forms of distress and can cause fear, anxiety, depression, and fatigue.

SCALE B — EMOTIONAL STRESSORS

People scoring low on this scale sometimes suffer from mild emotional distress that often gives way to more harmful types of stress. In times of change that drastically alters their normal pattern of living, people become emotionally upset and experience fear, anxiety, and sometimes depression. This can often lead to severe anxiety problems, major depression, and disorientation.

SCALE C — BEHAVIORAL STRESSORS

People scoring low on this scale sometimes suffer from difficulty remaining still, recurring interpersonal conflict, lashing out at other people, and difficulty maintaining focus on one activity very long. They tend to be compulsive and make decisions on the spur-of-the-moment. They are short tempered and find themselves verbally attacking other people.

SCALE D — PHYSICAL STRESSORS

People scoring low on this scale sometimes find themselves biting their nails, clenching their fists, and tapping their feet compulsively. This stress is conveyed in how they move and hold their body. They often find it difficult to sleep and start to lose interest in sleeping. The stress shows itself in their body in terms of neck and back pain, dryness of the mouth, nervous twitches, and constipation.

Stress can manifest itself in a variety of ways. Remember that a little bit of stress can be positive, but too much stress can affect your general wellness and your health. Regardless of your score on the LSS, the following exercises have been designed to help you manage your stress. Try doing all of the stress-management techniques that follow, then choose the ones you feel most comfortable doing.

©2005 Wellness Reproductions & Publishing 1.800.669.9208

EXERCISES for STRESS REDUCTION

1. STAYING IN THE PRESENT

Much of the stress that you are experiencing comes from dwelling on the past or worrying about future events. To reduce and ultimately stop these thoughts, you need to start living in the present moment. When you do this, all your attention becomes focused on what you are currently doing. When this happens, all worries, fears, and desires cease to enter your consciousness. As you begin to focus your attention, you will notice that thoughts of the past and future will arise. When they do, note it and gently turn your awareness back to the present.

EXPERIENTIAL EXERCISE — STAYING IN THE PRESENT
Try the following exercise to see how easy it is for you to relax. Sit still for several minutes and try to quiet your logical mind. Close your eyes and stop the internal chatter going on in your mind. Let go or block out any interfering thoughts, anxieties or emotions that pop into your head. Try not to think about the past or the future. After several minutes, open your eyes and answer the following questions:

What do you begin to notice as you attempt to keep your thoughts in the present?

_____

_____

How difficult was it to stay in the present? Why?

_____

_____

What thoughts kept popping into your head?

_____

_____

What emotions kept popping into your head?

_____

_____

How hard was this exercise? What could have made it easier?

_____

_____

EXERCISES for STRESS REDUCTION

2. MINDFULNESS

Mindfulness is that state of mind in which you are fully present and not thinking about other issues in your life. It is being in touch with the present moment so that you can see its fullness, hold it in your awareness, and come to know and understand it fully. It is being present to what you are doing at the time you are doing it in a nonjudgmental way. The type of attention associated with mindfulness increases your awareness and clarity. It allows you to accept the reality of the present moment. When you lose awareness of the present moment, you create problems for yourself because you are forced to rely on unconscious and automatic thoughts and behaviors that have developed over the years.

Mindfulness is more difficult than it sounds. Many forces work against you being mindful during any activity. Some of these forces are the creations of your own mind and include labels you attach to your performance, rehearsing what you might say next rather than listening, and judging yourself. Remind yourself that this present moment is all there is. What is happening now is simply happening. When asked "Are you aware?" or "Where is your mind right now?" you will observe that your mind has a habit of trying to escape from the present moment. However, mindfulness is the state of mind in which you are fully present with the person or the activity in which you are engaged.

EXPERIENTIAL EXERCISE — BEING MINDFUL
Stop for a moment. Sit down and become aware of your breathing. It doesn't matter for how long. Let go and fully accept the present moment. For several minutes, don't try to change anything, just let go and breathe. Breathe and be still. Give yourself permission to allow these moments to be as they are. Just let go and fully accept the present moment. If that does not work, focus your attention on any object for several minutes. Pick out an object and stare at it for several minutes. Now answer the following questions related to the mindfulness exercise you just completed.

What did you find your mind thinking about?

_____

_____

_____

_____

(Continued on page 11)

©2005 Wellness Reproductions & Publishing 1.800.669.9208

EXERCISES for STRESS REDUCTION

2. MINDFULNESS (cont'd)

What thoughts kept coming back into your head?

_____

_____

_____

_____

How did your mind attempt to escape the mindfulness of the present moment?

_____

_____

_____

_____

One of the reasons your mind attempts to escape the present moment is the fear of being mindful. Your mind would prefer you to be thinking about the past, which you cannot control, and the future, which has not yet, and may never, come. Don't get caught up at this point in having a special experience or in making some sort of progress. You will slowly notice differences in your awareness over time.

©2005 Wellness Reproductions & Publishing 1.800.669.9208

EXERCISES for STRESS REDUCTION

3. AFFIRMATIONS

Probably the best tool for you to use in quieting your logical mind is the use of affirmations. Affirmations are phrases you can use to reprogram your mind. They are brief statements that put you in the proper frame of mind to accept intuitive inputs. Affirmations are a way of sending your brain a message that the desired result has already been achieved. What you state, in the present tense, can easily be achieved. Examples of affirmations that might be used in helping to accept intuitive inputs include:

"I am able to manage my stress very effectively."

"My stress is disappearing."

"I will not let stress take over my life."

"I have control over the stress in my life."

EXPERIENTIAL EXERCISE - AFFIRMATIONS
Using the examples of affirmations above, formulate some of your own affirmations below:

_____

_____

To strengthen your coping skills in stressful situations, you need to practice your affirmations on a daily basis. Select one of the affirmations that you feel comfortable with and repeat the affirmation for about five minutes each day for one week. An example might be, To center myself, I am working on the following affirmation: "I have control over the stress in my life." Repeat your affirmation for five minutes each day for one week and then record your observations in the spaces below:

My affirmation is:

_____

_____

My observations include:

_____

_____

How my ability to cope with stress is increasing:

_____

_____

©2005 Wellness Reproductions & Publishing 1.800.669.9208

EXERCISES for STRESS REDUCTION

4. VISUALIZATION

Visualization, also called mental or guided imagery, can be used to reduce mental activity and manage stress. This method is used to induce deep relaxation and relieve tension.

EXPERIENTIAL EXERCISES — VISUALIZATION

Close your eyes and imagine yourself walking with someone through the forest. You can hear the wind swishing through the trees as you walk and feel the wind gently touching your face. You can hear birds singing and see the deep blue sky above the trees. As you continue walking you find a small patch of grass alongside a beautiful lake. You walk toward the lake and find yourself in the middle of a small patch of grass. It is very quiet here, the water is perfectly calm, and the grass feels soft below your feet. You lie down on the grass so that you can feel the sun on your face. You are completely relaxed, at peace with yourself and the world. It is quiet and you feel yourself drifting off to sleep. Allow your mind to take in the smells and sounds of this relaxing place.

How do you feel after completing this visualization?

_____

_____

_____

_____

What other places can you imagine that would be as relaxing (beach, mountain top, etc.)? Why?

_____

_____

_____

_____

What did you learn from this exercise?

_____

_____

_____

EXERCISES for STRESS REDUCTION

5. BREATHING

Because breath is vital to life itself, proper breathing is very important and can even be an excellent form of stress reduction. The pace at which you breathe and the depth of your breathing are vital in relaxation and stress reduction. When you encounter stressful situations, your breathing quickens and becomes more shallow. Breathing can also help to relax and quiet your body. Diaphragmatic breathing, in which you take in long, very deep breaths, is an especially powerful tool for relaxation. In diaphragmatic breathing, you push out your stomach and draw in a long deep breath. Then you exhale as slowly and as long as possible. Repeat this until relaxation occurs.

EXPERIENTIAL EXERCISE — BREATHING
Pay attention to your breathing. Don't try to change it, but just become more aware of it. This will allow you to easily be brought into conscious awareness. Make note of the parts of your body or ways your mind is attempting to interfere with the natural movement of your breathing. If your attention wanders and takes you away from the focus on your breathing, simply bring back your attention so that you return to your focus. Dwell on the rise and fall of your chest as you inhale and exhale. Simply allow your attention to settle you and stop distracting thoughts.

What do you notice about your breathing as you begin to attend to it?

_____

_____

_____

_____

_____

_____

_____

_____

©2005 Wellness Reproductions & Publishing 1.800.669.9208

EXERCISES for STRESS REDUCTION

6. EXERCISE

Exercise is another excellent method for combating and managing stress. In our society, the time needed to exercise is often very hard to find, but it is very important that you put aside time each week in order to exercise your body and relieve tension. Several different types of exercises are available for you to use in reducing stress:

— Aerobic Exercise uses sustained, rhythmic activity involving primarily the large muscles in your legs. Aerobic exercises include such activities as jogging, running, brisk walking, swimming, bicycling, kickboxing, or other high intensity martial arts and aerobic training. The goal of aerobic exercise is to gradually increase your stamina and enhance your cardiovascular system.

Which of the above aerobic exercises are you interested in doing to reduce the stress in your life?

_____

_____

_____

_____

— Low Intensity Exercise is used to increase muscle strength, enhance flexibility and quiet your mind. Low intensity exercises include slow walking, light gardening, yoga, walking in the woods, calisthenics, and "soft" martial arts like Tai Chi.

Which of the above low intensity exercises are you interested in doing to reduce the stress in your life?

_____

_____

_____

_____

EXERCISES for STRESS REDUCTION

7. PROGRESSIVE RELAXATION

Progressive relaxation helps you to bring relaxation to all parts of your body through concentrated awareness. It allows you to actually produce relaxation by focusing self-suggestions of warmth and relaxation in specific muscle groups throughout the body.

EXPERIENTIAL EXERCISE — PROGRESSIVE RELAXATION

Sit in a comfortable position. Close your eyes and start to feel your body relaxing. Think of yourself as a rag doll. Let the relaxation pass through each organ and body part you have. In this exercise, start with your feet and progressively relax all the parts of your body. This will help you to manage your stress effectively. Begin by having your body progressively relax with such statements as:

"I am relaxing my feet...   My feet are warm...   My feet are relaxed."
"I am relaxing my ankles...   My ankles are warm...   My ankles are relaxed."
"I am relaxing my calves...   My calves are warm...   My calves are relaxed."

Do this with the rest of your body until you are totally relaxed from your head to your feet. Block any distractions out of your mind as you concentrate on relaxing your entire body.

8. MEDITATION

Meditation is the practice of attempting to focus your attention on one thing at a time. It is a method in which you use repeated mental focus to quiet your mind, which in turn quiets your body. In meditation, focusing on one thing allows your mind to stay concentrated and excludes all other thoughts. There are many different forms of meditation. In meditation you can focus by repeating a word like "OM;" count your breaths by saying "one," "two," "three" after you exhale with each breath; or gaze at an object like a candle or a piece of wood without thinking about it in words.

9. BODY AWARENESS

Sit back for a few minutes and tune in to the sensations present in your body. Don't attempt to change any of these sensations, just become aware of them. Pay particular attention to the parts of your body that feel tense. Now notice the parts of your body that feel relaxed. Remain focused on your physical sensations for a few minutes and make note of things that come into your awareness that have not been present before.

Focus on things around you by completing the following sentence:
Right now, I am aware of the following things:

_____

Now focus on body sensations by completing the following sentence:
I am aware of the following things about my body:

_____

©2005 Wellness Reproductions & Publishing 1.800.669.9208

EXERCISES for STRESS REDUCTION

10. NUTRITION

Many people admit that during high stress periods they eat more than usual and eat less healthy foods. A poor diet contributes negatively to your reactions to stress and stressful situations. Although there is no best diet for every person, following are some general guidelines to help you eat healthier at all times:

- Reduce the fat in your diet
- Eat a balanced diet with sufficient calories, vitamins and minerals
- Do not eat excessive amounts
- Reduce cholesterol consumption
- Increase consumption of protein sources such as fish, poultry, nuts, lean meats, and low fat dairy products
- Eat foods low in sodium
- Eat less foods with high amounts of refined sugar
- Avoid excessive alcohol consumption
- Eat plenty of fruits and vegetables
- Be aware of how stress affects your personal eating habits

EXPERIENTIAL EXERCISE — NUTRITION

What types of food do you want to eat more of?

_____

_____

What types of food do you want to eat less of?

_____

_____

What other changes do you want to make in your diet?

_____

_____

What changes can you make in how you eat (eat more regularly, eat more slowly, eat smaller portions, etc.)?

_____

_____

EXERCISES for STRESS REDUCTION

11. THOUGHT STOPPING

Whenever you notice an anxiety-producing thought entering your stream-of-consciousness, internally shout the word "stop" to yourself.

EXPERIENTIAL EXERCISE — THOUGHT STOPPING
Close your eyes and imagine a situation in which a stressful thought often occurs. This might be a situation like talking in front of a group of people you do not know, going on a date, or going to a meeting at work. About thirty seconds after you begin to think about the situation, shout "stop" as the thought begins to enter your consciousness. Eventually, with some practice, you will be able to imagine hearing the word "stop" shouted inside your head.

What situation is stressful for you?

_____

_____

What do you notice about the stress after you use this thought-stopping technique to reduce stress?

_____

_____

12. LISTEN TO MUSIC

Listening to music is probably one of the easiest forms of relaxation. To benefit from the relaxation of music, you should select music that is soothing and that you find peaceful. To benefit the most from your music relaxation sessions, you should find approximately one-half hour of uninterrupted time by yourself daily.

EXPERIENTIAL EXERCISE — LISTENING TO MUSIC
Put on the music you want to listen to, find and settle into a comfortable position and close your eyes. Allow your entire body to begin to relax. Simply focus your attention on the music being played. If unrelated thoughts enter into your head, make a note of it and discard the thoughts. Allow all thoughts to disappear from your mind. You can use affirmations such as "music relaxes me" to enhance your relaxation.

How does your body feel different after listening to music?

_____

_____

How has your mood changed?

_____

©2005 Wellness Reproductions & Publishing 1.800.669.9208

PLANS for STRESS MANAGEMENT

Stress-management techniques I have utilized in the past:

_____

_____

_____

New stress-management techniques I would like to try:

_____

_____

_____

Steps I will take to begin using the new stress-management techniques:

_____

_____

_____

When and how I will practice these new stress-management techniques:

_____

_____

_____

Results I hope to achieve:

_____

_____

_____

How I will know when I am successful:

_____

_____

_____

GROUP ACTIVITY

PREPARATION:

1 Prepare flipcharts and markers.

2 Write on the flipchart the word "Stress."

3 Give each group member a piece of paper and pen.

SESSION:

1 Discuss with group members the meaning of stress. Describe the various types of stress and how stress affects your mind and your body. (3 minutes)

2 Write this question on the flipchart and ask group members, "How do you know when you are experiencing stress?" Give group members a few minutes to jot down ideas. Share and write all responses on the flipchart. (5 minutes)

3 Write the four different categories of stress symptoms on the board. On the flipchart write the words "Cognitive," "Emotional," "Behavioral" and "Physical." Share with people that these are the four primary ways that stress is encountered by all people. (5 minutes)

4 Break group participants into smaller groups. Ask group members to help each other identify stress-management techniques that will be most helpful to control their stress:

- Which stress-management techniques will help with cognitive symptoms?

- Which stress-management techniques will help with emotional symptoms?

- Which stress-management techniques will help with behavioral symptoms?

- Which stress-management techniques will help with physical symptoms?
  (10 minutes)

5 Reconvene in larger group and share experiences. (10 minutes)

6 Ask group members to share personal insights gained from this activity. (10 minutes)

©2005 Wellness Reproductions & Publishing 1.800.669.9208

STRESS CONTRACT

I, _____, am willing to take responsibility
for my personal health and wellness. I will incorporate wellness and
stress-management techniques into my lifestyle. I will make a
commitment to myself to:

_____

_____

_____

I will use the following stress-management techniques: _____

_____

_____

_____

I will do this (how often): _____

_____

_____

I will do this so that I: _____

_____

_____

_____   _____
Signature   Date

_____   _____
Witness   Date

©2005 Wellness Reproductions & Publishing 1.800.669.9208

TYPES of STRESS

● Sensory Deprivation — too little stimulation in a person's life

● Stress Overload — too much to do in the time available in a person's life

● Anticipatory Stress — stress related to an upcoming change, challenge, or crisis

● Residual Stress — stress that is an aftereffect of an event that has passed

● Built-Up Stress — stress that keeps compounding over time

● Negative Stress — stress related to an unanticipated event or crisis

● External Stress — stress related to the daily hassles of the physical environment (noise, confined spaces, bright lights)

PERSONAL INSIGHTS:

● _____

● _____

● _____

©2005 Wellness Reproductions & Publishing 1.800.669.9208

COMPONENTS of STRESS

● Stressor — A demand, circumstance, or situation that affects a person's equilibrium and evokes a stress response.

● Types of Stressors — The person encounters a stressor that might include such things as an illness, loss of a job, lack of financial resources, death of significant other, lack of purpose, or noise.

● Perception of the Stressor — How the person perceives each stressor is important in the effect it has. Because all people are different, the weight of a stressor varies from person to person.

● Physiological Response — Based on the person's perception of the stressor, a variety of bodily responses occur that are external manifestations of the stressor.

● Stress Management — The person relies on a variety of different tools and techniques to manage the stress.

PERSONAL INSIGHTS:

● _____

● _____

● _____

©2005 Wellness Reproductions & Publishing 1.800.669.9208

©2005 Wellness Reproductions & Publishing 1.800.669.9208

HEALTHY LIFESTYLE MODULE

The Healthy Lifestyle Inventory helps people identify the dimensions of their life in which they have a sense of wellness, and those in which they do not.

INDEX

Answers to the Pre- and Post-Test — Page 25:	
1. Health and wellness are the same thing	False
2. Wellness is a process of preventing disease	True
3. Spirituality is not a critical aspect of wellness	False
4. Wellness can help a person adapt to changing circumstances	False
5. Wellness can reduce your risk of chronic illness	True

©2005 Wellness Reproductions & Publishing 1.800.669.9208

HEALTHY LIFESTYLE INVENTORY

PRE- and POST-TEST

NAME: _____ DATE: _____

The following true-or-false questions are designed
to determine your knowledge about stress,
stress management and wellness.

Please circle Ⓣ if you think the statement is TRUE
and Ⓕ if you think the statement is FALSE.

---

1. Health and wellness are the same thing . . . . T   F

2. Wellness is a process of preventing disease . . . . T   F

3. Spirituality is not a critical aspect of wellness . . . . T   F

4. Wellness can help a person adapt to changing circumstances . . . . T   F

5. Wellness can reduce your risk of chronic illness . . . . T   F

©2005 Wellness Reproductions & Publishing 1.800.669.9208

HEALTHY LIFESTYLE INVENTORY

Name:

_____

_____

Gender:

_____

Date:

_____

Age:

_____

©2005 Wellness Reproductions & Publishing 1.800.669.9208

DIRECTIONS

Wellness has been described as the ability to live life to the fullest extent, to maximize your full potential, and to have a unique purpose in life. Wellness is a combination of mental, emotional, physical, social, spiritual and occupational well-being. A sense of wellness suggests that people are responsible for their own well-being and requires a deep commitment. The Healthy Lifestyle Inventory is designed to help you identify the dimensions of your life in which you have this sense of wellness.

This booklet contains 84 statements that are divided into six categories. Read each of the statements and decide how descriptive the statement is of you. In each of the choices listed, circle the number of your response on the line to the right of each statement.

In the following example, the circled 1 indicates the statement is not at all descriptive of the person completing the inventory:

4 = VERY DESCRIPTIVE	3 = SOMEWHAT DESCRIPTIVE	2 = A LITTLE DESCRIPTIVE	1 = NOT AT ALL DESCRIPTIVE

I. MENTAL WELLNESS
I am curious about things   4   3   2   (1)

This is not a test. Since there are no right or wrong answers, do not spend too much time thinking about your answers. Be sure to respond to every statement.

Turn to the next page and begin.

©2005 Wellness Reproductions & Publishing 1.800.669.9208

HEALTHY LIFESTYLE INVENTORY

4 = VERY DESCRIPTIVE	3 = SOMEWHAT DESCRIPTIVE	2 = A LITTLE DESCRIPTIVE	1 = NOT AT ALL DESCRIPTIVE

I. MENTAL WELLNESS:

	4	3	2	1
I am curious about things.	4	3	2	1
I am interested in continuing my education.	4	3	2	1
I am always looking for ways to learn more.	4	3	2	1
I pick up new concepts quickly.	4	3	2	1
I am creative.	4	3	2	1
I approach similar tasks in new and different ways.	4	3	2	1
I often take the initiative in things I do.	4	3	2	1
Unfamiliar situations do not bother me.	4	3	2	1
I desire to understand what life has to offer.	4	3	2	1
I have a good memory and use it to my advantage.	4	3	2	1
I am always trying to improve myself.	4	3	2	1
I am open-minded.	4	3	2	1
Rather than being intimidated by challenges, I perceive them as a chance to learn.	4	3	2	1

TOTAL = _____

II. EMOTIONAL WELLNESS

	4	3	2	1
I understand my own feelings.	4	3	2	1
I accept my physical and mental limitations.	4	3	2	1
I readily accept the emotions of others.	4	3	2	1
I am able to maintain intimate relationships with others.	4	3	2	1
I express my emotions appropriately.	4	3	2	1
I can adjust to change and cope with the stress of daily life.	4	3	2	1
I tend to be happy most of the time.	4	3	2	1
I have inner peace and contentment.	4	3	2	1
I take minor setbacks in stride.	4	3	2	1
I don't waste time or energy dwelling on the past.	4	3	2	1
I am able to stay focused on the present.	4	3	2	1
I value and accept myself.	4	3	2	1
I do not worry about failure.	4	3	2	1
I can easily forgive others.	4	3	2	1

TOTAL = _____

Turn to the next page and continue.

©2005 Wellness Reproductions & Publishing 1.800.669.9208

HEALTHY LIFESTYLE INVENTORY

4 = VERY DESCRIPTIVE	3 = SOMEWHAT DESCRIPTIVE	2 = A LITTLE DESCRIPTIVE	1 = NOT AT ALL DESCRIPTIVE

III. PHYSICAL WELLNESS

I eat a well-balanced diet.	4	3	2	1
I have an active lifestyle.	4	3	2	1
I have the energy I need to do things I like.	4	3	2	1
I respect and like my body.	4	3	2	1
I get plenty of exercise and physical activity.	4	3	2	1
I maintain a proper weight.	4	3	2	1
I get enough sleep each day.	4	3	2	1
I avoid risky sexual behaviors.	4	3	2	1
I do not use illegal drugs.	4	3	2	1
I do not drink alcohol.	4	3	2	1
I do not use cigarettes, cigars, or smokeless tobacco.	4	3	2	1
I take effective measures if I become sick.	4	3	2	1
I get regular physical examinations.	4	3	2	1
I limit my exposure to the sun and other harmful elements.	4	3	2	1

TOTAL = _____

IV. SOCIAL WELLNESS

I am outgoing and affectionate toward others.	4	3	2	1
I am concerned for humanity.	4	3	2	1
I am concerned for the environment.	4	3	2	1
I relate well to others in my family.	4	3	2	1
I relate well to others in my community.	4	3	2	1
I am tolerant of others.	4	3	2	1
I tend to openly share my thoughts and feelings with others.	4	3	2	1
I am able to develop and maintain intimacy.	4	3	2	1
I am loyal and faithful to family members.	4	3	2	1
I treat others with respect and fairness.	4	3	2	1
I like helping others.	4	3	2	1
I feel secure and confident about myself.	4	3	2	1
I find joy in working with others to accomplish tasks.	4	3	2	1
I am rarely jealous of other people.	4	3	2	1

TOTAL = _____

Turn to the next page and continue.

©2005 Wellness Reproductions & Publishing 1.800.669.9208

HEALTHY LIFESTYLE INVENTORY

4 = VERY DESCRIPTIVE	3 = SOMEWHAT DESCRIPTIVE	2 = A LITTLE DESCRIPTIVE	1 = NOT AT ALL DESCRIPTIVE

V. SPIRITUAL WELLNESS

	4	3	2	1
I am committed to worthwhile purposes.	4	3	2	1
I have faith that will sustain me regardless of what happens.	4	3	2	1
I am able to find purpose in my life.	4	3	2	1
I am good at "seeing the whole picture."	4	3	2	1
I set and work toward realistic goals.	4	3	2	1
I am enthusiastic about what is to come.	4	3	2	1
I don't dwell on discouragement and failure.	4	3	2	1
My life has meaning and direction.	4	3	2	1
I believe that some power brings humanity together.	4	3	2	1
I always search for greater value in life.	4	3	2	1
I believe in a power greater than myself.	4	3	2	1
I am concerned about self-actualization in my life.	4	3	2	1
I believe that I am a spiritual person.	4	3	2	1
I treat all people and animals ethically.	4	3	2	1

TOTAL = _____

VI. OCCUPATIONAL WELLNESS

	4	3	2	1
My job provides rewards that are important to me.	4	3	2	1
I have authority over how I perform my job.	4	3	2	1
My job provides a lot of new and exciting challenges.	4	3	2	1
I am able to use my skills at work.	4	3	2	1
I have the opportunity to learn new skills at work.	4	3	2	1
My job provides an opportunity for advancement.	4	3	2	1
My job provides an opportunity for recognition.	4	3	2	1
I have a sense of control at work.	4	3	2	1
I have access to feedback from management.	4	3	2	1
I get support from my co-workers.	4	3	2	1
I am free of safety hazards at work.	4	3	2	1
I work the number of hours I want to work.	4	3	2	1
I always know what my supervisor expects of me.	4	3	2	1
I feel appreciated at work.	4	3	2	1

TOTAL = _____

Go to the scoring directions on the next page.

©2005 Wellness Reproductions & Publishing 1.800.669.9208

SCORING

Wellness is often conceptualized as consisting of six diverse dimensions including mental wellness, emotional wellness, physical wellness, social wellness, spiritual wellness, and occupational wellness. The Healthy Lifestyle Inventory is designed to measure how well you really are. For each of the six sections on the previous pages, count the scores you circled for each of the six sections. Put that total on the line marked "Total" at the end of each section.

Then, transfer your totals to the spaces below:

MENTAL WELLNESS TOTAL = _____

EMOTIONAL WELLNESS TOTAL = _____

PHYSICAL WELLNESS TOTAL = _____

SOCIAL WELLNESS TOTAL = _____

SPIRITUAL WELLNESS TOTAL = _____

OCCUPATIONAL WELLNESS TOTAL = _____

PROFILE INTERPRETATION

SCORES FROM 14 TO 27 on any of the above scales are LOW and indicate that you do not have a sense of wellness in those areas.

SCORES FROM 28 TO 42 on any of the above scales are AVERAGE and indicate that you have a sense of wellness similar to others taking this assessment.

SCORES FROM 43 TO 56 on any of the above scale are HIGH and indicate that you have a good sense of wellness in those areas.

©2005 Wellness Reproductions & Publishing 1.800.669.9208

MENTAL DIMENSION

People who are mentally well ensure that their minds are engaged in lively interaction with the world. They believe that learning never stops and they demonstrate a natural curiosity about themselves and about the world in which they live. They are able to think clearly, learn new concepts and ideas and embrace the opportunity to learn more. They have great common sense, but also are logical and are able to reason well. They have a genuine sense of curiosity that allows them to accept new challenges. They have an interest in understanding the world around them. They are alert and bright and use their memory to their advantage. They value the opportunity to improve themselves and learn new things. They are open-minded and accept the differences of others. They are faithful to their own philosophies and ideas, and are willing to share these with other people.

What would you like to learn more about?

_____

_____

What subjects are you curious about but never examined?

_____

_____

What could you learn to improve yourself?

_____

_____

In what situations are you logical?

_____

_____

In what situations are you creative?

_____

_____

What can you do to increase your mental wellness?

_____

_____

©2005 Wellness Reproductions & Publishing 1.800.669.9208

EMOTIONAL DIMENSION

People who are emotionally well have the ability to understand their own feelings. By doing so, they accept their limitations, enhance their emotional stability, accept the emotions of others and maintain effective relationships with others. They are able to express their emotions appropriately and adjust to change quickly and easily. They have a deep sense of happiness and inner contentment. They feel loved themselves and love other people. They know how to laugh and do so as often as they can. They focus their energy in the present and have a strong sense of optimism. They are goal-oriented but still enjoy themselves in the present. They accept themselves and value what they have to contribute to the world. They are able to enjoy their successes, make the best of the circumstances and move beyond their failures. They are deeply in touch with their own feelings, accept themselves and cherish the differences in others. They are responsible for their own happiness and do not blame others when they are unhappy.

What are your limitations?

_____

_____

How do you contribute to the world?

_____

_____

What makes you happiest?

_____

_____

What emotions do you express well?

_____

_____

What emotions do you have difficulty expressing?

_____

_____

What do you love about yourself?

_____

_____

What can you do to increase your emotional wellness?

_____

_____

©2005 Wellness Reproductions & Publishing 1.800.669.9208

PHYSICAL DIMENSION

People who are physically well eat a balanced diet, get plenty of sleep, exercise and get enough physical activity, and restrict the intake of such substances as tobacco, caffeine, alcohol and drugs. They have an active lifestyle and enjoy being outdoors. They have plenty of energy to do the things they enjoy as well as the energy to complete demanding work on the job. They both respect and like their own bodies. They are confident and optimistic about being able to take care of their bodies and their health problems. They are proactive in maintaining their health and get regular physical exams. They are resistant to disease because they get a proper combination of exercise, nutrition, sleep and relaxation. They tend to be physically fit, strong and have great endurance. They tend to make the most of their body and take interest and delight in it.

How do you protect your physical health?

_____

_____

How do you maintain physical health through exercise?

_____

_____

How do you maintain physical health through nutrition?

_____

_____

How do you maintain physical health through sleep?

_____

_____

Do you have an active lifestyle? If yes, describe it. If no, explain why not.

_____

_____

What can you do to increase your physical wellness?

_____

_____

SOCIAL DIMENSION

People who are socially well are friendly, concerned about others, outgoing and affectionate. They are interested in other people, in humanity in general and in the environment. They relate well to others, care about others less fortunate than themselves and are able to put themselves in the shoes of others to better understand their world. They are respectful and tolerant of others who may be different from them. They are quite able to develop intimacy with others, are very trustworthy and loyal to both their family and others outside the family. They make friends easily and treat them fairly and with respect. They are "people" people who are able to develop the spirit of teamwork and cooperation with those around them. They rarely view others with jealousy or suspicion. They are rarely competitive and attempt to outdo or put others down. They enjoy mutual support and work together to accomplish mutual goals. They love themselves but never have a self-centered view of themselves. They enjoy reaching out and being with other people.

How do you show your interest in other people?

_____

_____

How are you cooperative with those around you?

_____

_____

How do you develop and maintain intimacy with others?

_____

_____

How do you handle conflict?

_____

_____

What can you do to increase your social wellness?

_____

_____

©2005 Wellness Reproductions & Publishing 1.800.669.9208

SPIRITUAL DIMENSION

People who are spiritually well are committed to meaning and purpose in life, faith, and peace in the world. They have a high degree of meaning and direction in their lives. They are continually searching for the truth and for greater values in life. Their life is directed toward meaningful life and career goals. They may believe that some greater power – whether it be nature, religion, science or a Higher Power – is responsible for creation and ultimately brings together all of humanity. Their life is characterized by optimism, values, and a hope that sustains them through good times and bad times. They make a concerted effort to develop their inner selves and identify a core theme to direct their lives. They are able to discover, identify and act on their core purpose. They are able to see the "big picture" in life and act accordingly. They set reasonable goals and dedicate their lives to achieving these goals with optimism and perseverance. They are enthused about what lies ahead, yet live in the present and accept their past. They rarely dwell on disappointments they have had, but rather continue to look for their next goal that will make their life more purposeful.

What values and morals guide you and your behavior?

_____

_____

Do you believe in a Higher Power? What form does this Higher Power take?

_____

_____

How have you been trying to develop your inner self?

_____

_____

What do you feel is your purpose in life?

_____

_____

What goals have you set for yourself in the future?

_____

_____

What can you do to increase your spiritual wellness?

_____

_____

OCCUPATIONAL DIMENSION

People who are occupationally well work for rewards that are important to them. They are able to maximize their skills and potential, and use their work as an opportunity to broaden their skill base and learn new skills. They enjoy both the routine aspects of their work as well as the unpredictable challenges that occur at work. They seek opportunities for advancement and recognition but do not base their self-esteem on these factors. They feel like they have control on the job as they often participate in the planning and management policies and procedures, are able to give and receive appropriate feedback and can adequately use the technology available to them. They feel a sense of collaboration with management and with co-workers. They work in a job that is free from physical stressors, one that provides them with a sense of safety and security and one that provides a sense of belonging. They feel a heightened sense of self-esteem by doing the work at their job. They also have a satisfying balance between time and energy spent at work and the time and energy they spend with family and during leisure activities.

What do you value in the work you do?

_____

_____

How do you feel control at work? If you do not, why not?

_____

_____

If you are unemployed, how can you find employment?

_____

_____

What is it about work that gives you a heightened sense of self-esteem?

_____

_____

What are the best ways to balance work, family and leisure?

_____

_____

What can you do to increase your occupational wellness?

_____

_____

©2005 Wellness Reproductions & Publishing 1.800.669.9208

GROUP ACTIVITY

PREPARATION:

1 Prepare flipcharts and markers.

2 Write on the flipchart the words "Mental," "Emotional," "Physical," "Social," "Spiritual," and "Occupational."

3 Give each group member a piece of paper and pen.

SESSION:

1 Ask group members to think about words that describe each of the six words written on the flipchart. (3 minutes)

2 Ask group members, "What are several words that mean the same thing as Mental?" and write this question on the flipchart. Give group members a few minutes to jot down ideas. Share and write all responses on the flipchart. (3 minutes)

3 Ask group members, "What are several words that mean the same thing as Emotional?" and write this question on the flipchart. Give group members a few minutes to jot down ideas. Share and write all responses on the flipchart. (3 minutes)

4 Ask group members, "What are several words that mean the same thing as Physical?" and write this question on the flipchart. Give group members a few minutes to jot down ideas. Share and write all responses on the flipchart. (3 minutes)

5 Ask group members, "What are several words that mean the same thing as Social?" and write this question on the flipchart. Give group members a few minutes to jot down ideas. Share and write all responses on the flipchart. (3 minutes)

6 Ask group members, "What are several words that mean the same thing as Spiritual?" and write this question on the flipchart. Give group members a few minutes to jot down ideas. Share and write all responses on the flipchart. (3 minutes)

7 Ask group members, "What are several words that mean the same thing as Occupational?" and write this question on the flipchart. Give group members a few minutes to jot down ideas. Share and write all responses on the flipchart. (3 minutes)

8 Break group participants into smaller groups. Ask them to draw a pie. Then have them pretend that the six dimensions of wellness discussed are pieces of the pie. Have them decide as a group how big each of the pieces of the pie would be, based on which dimensions of life are most critical to wellness. (15 minutes)

9 Reconvene in larger group and share experiences. (10 minutes)

10 Process by asking one or more of the following questions: (10 minutes)
    Did your group agree on the size of each of the slices of pie?
    Which dimensions did your group feel was most important?
    Which dimensions did your group feel was least important?
    What did you learn about how you feel about the importance of the six dimensions?

BENEFITS OF WELLNESS

ACHIEVING A HIGH LEVEL OF WELLNESS HELPS YOU:

- ◼ have more energy to fight stress.

- ◼ feel and look better.

- ◼ recover quicker from illness or injury.

- ◼ function better in school, at work, or in relationships.

- ◼ turn problems into interesting challenges.

- ◼ be more confident and optimistic.

- ◼ feel hopeful rather than hopeless.

- ◼ reduce the possibility of chronic illness.

PERSONAL INSIGHTS:

- ◼ _____

- ◼ _____

- ◼ _____

©2005 Wellness Reproductions & Publishing 1.800.669.9208

SIGNS OF WELLNESS

- ■ Nonhurtful sense of humor
- ■ Sensitivity to the needs of self and others
- ■ Sense of spirituality or faith
- ■ Ability to adapt to changing situations
- ■ Interest in contributing to society
- ■ Positive outlook and expectations
- ■ Positive social support system
- ■ Interest in health and physical fitness
- ■ Interest in lifelong learning

PERSONAL INSIGHTS:

- ■ _____
- ■ _____
- ■ _____

WELLNESS COMPONENTS

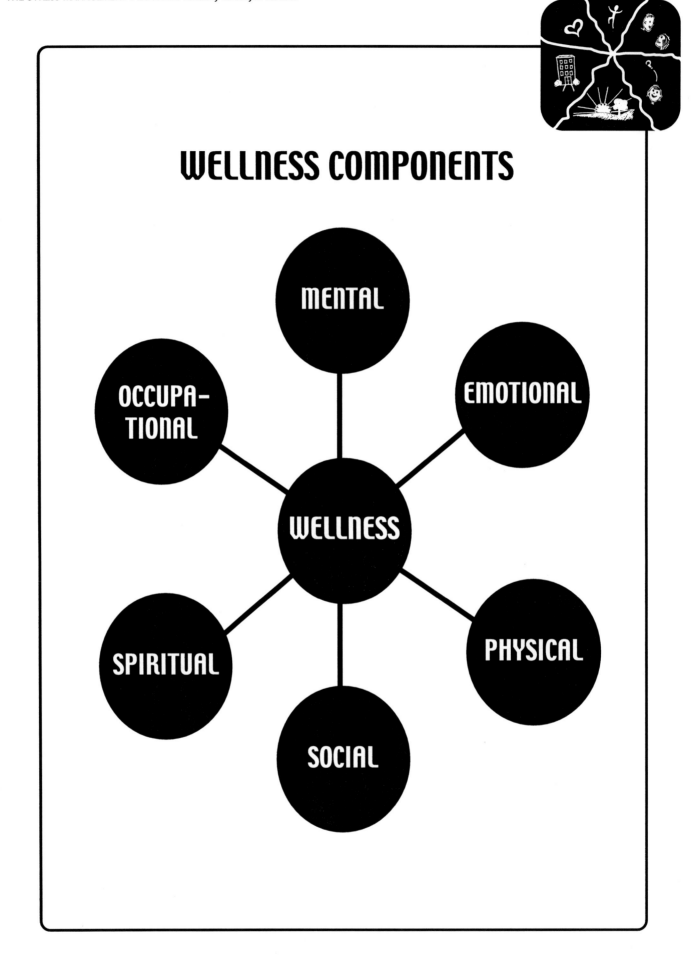

©2005 Wellness Reproductions & Publishing 1.800.669.9208

COPING with STRESS MODULE

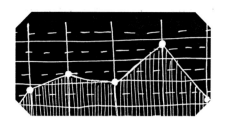

The Coping with Stress Inventory helps people identify their resources for coping with stress and change.

INDEX

Answers to the pre- and post-test — page 43:	
1. All people cope with stress in the same way	False
2. All people have a particular style of coping	True
3. Stress reduction is a way of coping with stress	True
4. Exercise is the way of coping with stress for most people	False
5. Coping means dealing constructively with a stressful event	True

COPING with STRESS SCALE

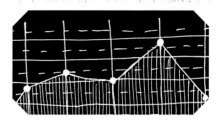

PRE- and POST-TEST

NAME: _____ DATE: _____

The following true-or-false questions
are designed to determine your knowledge
of stress and dealing with change.

Please circle (T) if you think the statement is TRUE
and (F) if you think the statement is FALSE.

---

1. All people cope with stress in the same way . . . . T   F

2. All people have a particular style of coping . . . . T   F

3. Stress reduction is a way of coping with stress . . . . T   F

4. Exercise is the way of coping with stress for most people . . . . T   F

5. Coping means dealing constructively with a stressful event . . . . T   F

©2005 Wellness Reproductions & Publishing 1.800.669.9208

COPING with STRESS SCALE

Name:

_____

_____

Gender:

_____

Date:

_____

Age:

_____

©2005 Wellness Reproductions & Publishing 1.800.669.9208

DIRECTIONS

Basic broad coping resources have been identified that seem to be important in dealing effectively with a variety of stressful situations. These stressful situations take many forms in many different life roles and could include dealing with the loss of a loved one, loss of a job or divorce. We are all able to cope differently with life and career stress by calling on different types of coping resources. The Coping with Stress Scale (CSS) will help you identify the specific resources you use, and those that you neglect, when dealing with the stress in your life.

In the following example, the circled numbers indicate how much the statement is descriptive of the person completing the inventory.

4 = VERY OFTEN	3 = OFTEN	2 = SOMETIMES	1 = NOT AT ALL

When I am in a stressful situation, I manage stress by:

1. Seeking help from a Higher Power   4   (3)   2   1
2. Looking for comfort in my religious beliefs   4   3   (2)   1

This is not a test. Since there are no right or wrong answers, do not spend too much time thinking about your answers. Be sure to respond to every statement.

Turn to the next page and begin.

©2005 Wellness Reproductions & Publishing 1.800.669.9208

COPING with STRESS SCALE

4 = VERY OFTEN	3 = OFTEN	2 = SOMETIMES	1 = NOT AT ALL

WHEN I AM IN A STRESSFUL SITUATION, I MANAGE STRESS BY:

I. SOCIAL-SUPPORT RESOURCES

	4	3	2	1
1. Asking people for their help.	4	3	2	1
2. Listening to others.	4	3	2	1
3. Using input from significant others in solving problems.	4	3	2	1
4. Spending time with helpful people.	4	3	2	1
5. Allowing people to help me during transition periods.	4	3	2	1
6. Identifying people who will support me.	4	3	2	1
7. Talking to others about my feelings.	4	3	2	1
TOTAL = _____				

II. PLANNING AND CHANGE

	4	3	2	1
8. Changing the stressful situation.	4	3	2	1
9. Developing a plan for new options and opportunities.	4	3	2	1
10. Changing my lifestyle (people I hang out with, amount of work I do, etc.).	4	3	2	1
11. Weighing the negative consequences of potential decisions.	4	3	2	1
12. Doing what needs to be done in a logical manner.	4	3	2	1
13. Identifying a plan about how to make changes in my life.	4	3	2	1
14. Implementing and executing the chosen courses of action.	4	3	2	1
TOTAL = _____				

Go on to the next page.

©2005 Wellness Reproductions & Publishing 1.800.669.9208

COPING with STRESS SCALE

4 = VERY OFTEN	3 = OFTEN	2 = SOMETIMES	1 = NOT AT ALL

WHEN I AM IN A STRESSFUL SITUATION, I MANAGE STRESS BY:

III. INTERNAL RESOURCES

	4	3	2	1
15. Using my personal strengths to create opportunities.	4	3	2	1
16. Converting negative thoughts about myself into positive ones.	4	3	2	1
17. Viewing transitions as opportunities for personal and professional growth.	4	3	2	1
18. Seeing stressful situations as a normal part of life.	4	3	2	1
19. Identifying and using my personal strengths.	4	3	2	1
20. Identifying negative thoughts I have about myself.	4	3	2	1
21. Changing my irrational beliefs about myself and the world.	4	3	2	1
TOTAL = _____				

IV. STRESS REDUCTION

	4	3	2	1
22. Practicing self-relaxation techniques (meditation, deep breathing, etc).	4	3	2	1
23. Running, jogging, or aerobic exercise.	4	3	2	1
24. Engaging in relaxing leisure activities.	4	3	2	1
25. Eating and sleeping well.	4	3	2	1
26. Managing my time better.	4	3	2	1
27. Doing progressive muscle relaxation or getting a massage.	4	3	2	1
28. Listening to music to reduce the stress.	4	3	2	1
TOTAL = _____				

Go on to the next page.

©2005 Wellness Reproductions & Publishing 1.800.669.9208

COPING with STRESS SCALE

4 = VERY OFTEN	3 = OFTEN	2 = SOMETIMES	1 = NOT AT ALL

WHEN I AM IN A STRESSFUL SITUATION, I MANAGE STRESS BY:

V. SPIRITUALITY RESOURCES

	4	3	2	1
29. Seeking help from a Higher Power.	4	3	2	1
30. Looking for comfort in my religious beliefs.	4	3	2	1
31. Speaking with a leader in my faith.	4	3	2	1
32. Praying for guidance, strength, or wisdom.	4	3	2	1
33. Recognizing what I can or cannot change.	4	3	2	1
34. Allowing my religion or spiritual path to transcend the stress.	4	3	2	1
35. Connecting with my true purpose in life.	4	3	2	1
TOTAL = _____				

VI. STRESS AVOIDANCE

	4	3	2	1
36. Trying not to sweat the "small" stuff.	4	3	2	1
37. Going to the movies or watching television to think less about it.	4	3	2	1
38. Working more to take my mind off it.	4	3	2	1
39. Trying not to overcommit myself to too many tasks.	4	3	2	1
40. Being more assertive with friends and significant others.	4	3	2	1
41. Trying not to put myself in potentially stressful situations.	4	3	2	1
42. Reminding myself to be more content with what I have in life and career.	4	3	2	1
TOTAL = _____				

Go to the scoring directions on the next page.

©2005 Wellness Reproductions & Publishing 1.800.669.9208

SCORING DIRECTIONS

The Coping with Stress Scale is designed to measure the strength of your ability to cope with transitions in your life. For each of the sections on the previous three pages, count the scores you circled for each of the four sections. Put that total on the line marked "TOTAL" at the end of each section.

Then, transfer your totals to the spaces below:

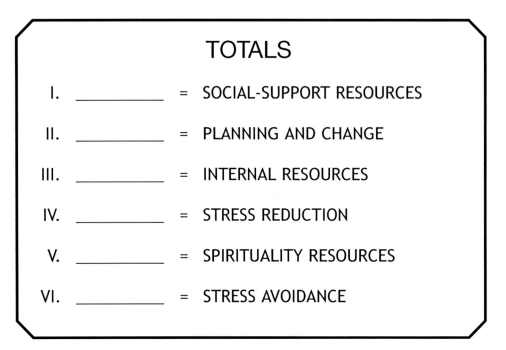

TOTALS

I. _____ = SOCIAL-SUPPORT RESOURCES

II. _____ = PLANNING AND CHANGE

III. _____ = INTERNAL RESOURCES

IV. _____ = STRESS REDUCTION

V. _____ = SPIRITUALITY RESOURCES

VI. _____ = STRESS AVOIDANCE

PROFILE INTERPRETATION

SCORES FROM 7 TO 13 ARE LOW and mean that you often fail to use the skills from this scale in coping successfully with the stress in your life.

SCORES FROM 14 TO 21 ARE AVERAGE and mean that you use coping skills from this scale that are similar to those of most other people.

SCORES FROM 22 TO 28 ARE HIGH and mean that you often use the skills from this scale in coping successfully with the stress in your life.

Any scales on which you scored in the "Low" or "Average" ranges may be found on the pages that follow. Then, read the description and complete the exercises that are included. These exercises will help you develop more effective coping skills.

©2005 Wellness Reproductions & Publishing 1.800.669.9208

I. SOCIAL-SUPPORT RESOURCES

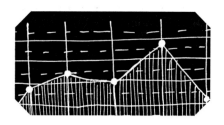

People scoring high on this scale tend to attempt to get advice from significant others in helping them deal with stress. In order to reduce the stress, they will attempt to share their experiences with others who have been in similar situations or have had similar types of stressful experiences. They often seek emotional support from friends and loved ones to whom they can talk about how they feel.

Who are the people who will support you in life?

_____

_____

_____

_____

How can these people help you reach your goals?

_____

_____

_____

_____

_____

What social skills must you develop to cultivate your support system?

_____

_____

_____

_____

©2005 Wellness Reproductions & Publishing 1.800.669.9208

II. PLANNING and CHANGE

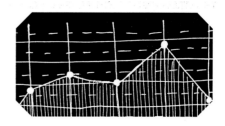

For people scoring high in this category, planning and change are exhibited through the decisions they make during times of stress. They may experience feelings of hesitation and anxiety about decisions, but they are able to use a rational approach to decision-making and implementing change. They concentrate their efforts on doing something about the stressful situation. They develop a strategy about what to do, make a plan of action, and then take the necessary steps to reduce the stress they are encountering.

How do you make decisions? What is your decision-making style?

_____

_____

_____

_____

What are your greatest planning skills?

_____

_____

_____

_____

How do you develop a plan for dealing with stressful situations?

_____

_____

_____

_____

©2005 Wellness Reproductions & Publishing 1.800.669.9208

III. INTERNAL RESOURCES

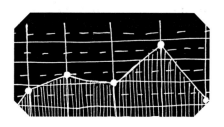

People scoring high in this category use internal self-talk to provide critical and supportive messages during a transition. They can do this by becoming more aware of the cognitive distortions and irrational thoughts that lead to feelings of frustration and depression. In addition, they can visualize themselves as they would like to be. They are able to turn threats into opportunities and look at stressful situations as learning experiences.

What are your greatest strengths?

_____

_____

_____

_____

How would you describe yourself?

_____

_____

_____

_____

How do others describe you?

_____

_____

_____

_____

©2005 Wellness Reproductions & Publishing 1.800.669.9208

IV. STRESS REDUCTION

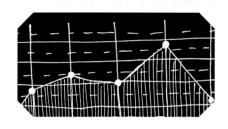

People scoring high in this category are able to identify symptoms of distress and effectively respond to stress. They can use a variety of methods for managing stress including meditating, getting more sleep, eating more nutritiously, breathing rhythmically, exercising, doing self-hypnosis, setting priorities and cognitive restructuring.

How do you relax when you are in a stressful situation?

_____

_____

_____

_____

What emotions do you experience during periods of stress?

_____

_____

_____

_____

What new relaxation techniques do you want to learn?

_____

_____

_____

_____

©2005 Wellness Reproductions & Publishing 1.800.669.9208

V. SPIRITUALITY RESOURCES

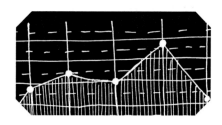

People scoring high on this scale tend to seek help from their religion or spirituality. They find comfort in religion and spirituality in their attempts to cope. They are excited about what lies ahead in their lives and are not merely content with their accomplishments from the past.

What religious practices or spiritual resources do you use to help reduce stress?

_____

_____

_____

_____

What are two of your religious or spiritual beliefs?

_____

_____

_____

_____

How does your religious or spiritual practice support you in relieving stress?

_____

_____

_____

_____

©2005 Wellness Reproductions & Publishing 1.800.669.9208

VI. STRESS AVOIDANCE

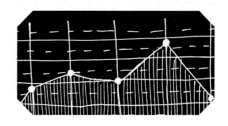

People scoring high in this category look for alternatives to facing stressful situations. They have the ability to avoid and reduce the effects of stress. They are skilled in finding ways to avoid the thoughts and emotions associated with stress. They tend to assess the gains and costs of dealing with the stress and often believe that the stressor is not happening to them or they act as though it hasn't happened to them. They may even look to other substitute activities to take their mind off the stress. They may engage in work and leisure behaviors to help them transcend the stressful situation.

How do you attempt to avoid stress?

_____

_____

_____

_____

What types of things do you say to yourself?

_____

_____

_____

_____

What unhealthy habits are you afraid of developing in your attempts to avoid stress?

_____

_____

_____

_____

©2005 Wellness Reproductions & Publishing 1.800.669.9208

GROUP ACTIVITY

PREPARATION:

1 Prepare a flipchart.

2 Cut out pictures of people coping with stress, using such resources as spirituality, social support, internal resources, stress reduction, planning and change and stress avoidance.

3 Paste these pictures on the flipchart.

SESSION:

1 Explain to the group members that the ability to cope with stress is a skill that can be learned. The more resources we have at our disposal and can easily use, the better we are able to cope with stress. (3 minutes)

2 Show the pictures of people using the various coping skills on the flipchart. Ask group members to identify which of the coping skills is being used. Give group members a few minutes to jot down ideas. Share and write all responses on the flipchart. (5 minutes)

3 Break group participants into smaller groups. Within each of the smaller groups:

- Ask people to identify which of the coping skills they use most.

- Ask people to identify which of the coping skills they use least.

- Have people brainstorm ways in which each person can further develop additional resources for coping with stress. (20 minutes)

4 Reconvene in larger group and share experiences. (10 minutes)

5 Process by asking one or more of the following questions:

a) Which coping skills were identified most?

b) Which coping skills were identified least?

c) Which coping skills would you like to develop? (10 minutes)

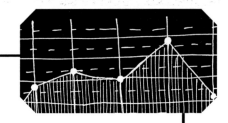

COPING RESOURCES

- Do relaxation exercises
- Curb negative self-talk
- Use your support system
- Remain optimistic
- Improve your communication skills
- Use community services
- Improve your problem-solving skills
- Look to your faith and spirituality
- Change your lifestyle
- Take your mind off the stress

PERSONAL INSIGHTS:

- _____
- _____
- _____

©2005 Wellness Reproductions & Publishing 1.800.669.9208

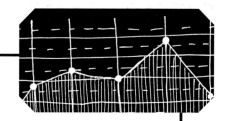

STAGES OF COPING

■ **STAGE 1 – Appraisal of Stress**
What is the stressor?

Is it worth being stressed about?

■ **STAGE 2 – My Resources**
What resources do I have for coping with the stressor?

What previous experiences do I have with this type of stress?

What are my beliefs about myself?

What are my beliefs about the environment?

What available personal resources do I have?

What available external resources do I have (money, social support)?

■ **STAGE 3 – Coping**
What actions can I take?

PERSONAL INSIGHTS:

■ _____

■ _____

■ _____

©2005 Wellness Reproductions & Publishing 1.800.669.9208

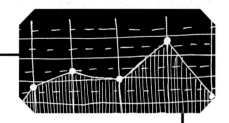

RESULTS OF EFFECTIVE COPING

People who are effective at coping with stress:

◼ manage their feelings effectively.

◼ feel "in charge" of their life.

◼ handle similar situations confidently.

◼ learn from their mistakes.

◼ reject unfounded criticism.

◼ value themselves as "special" human beings.

◼ accept praise and recognition from others.

PERSONAL INSIGHTS:

◼ _____

◼ _____

◼ _____

©2005 Wellness Reproductions & Publishing 1.800.669.9208

RESILIENT PERSONALITY MODULE

The Resilient Personality Inventory helps people identify how hardy they are in times of stress and change.

INDEX

Answers to the pre- and post-test — page 61:	
1. Resilient people are hardy	True
2. Resilient people never experience stress	False
3. Your level of resiliency can never be changed	False
4. Hardiness is the ability to stay well even with lots of stress	True
5. Hardiness allows you to view change as an opportunity	True

©2005 Wellness Reproductions & Publishing 1.800.669.9208

RESILIENT PERSONALITY INVENTORY

PRE- and POST-TEST

NAME: _____ DATE: _____

The following true-or-false questions
are designed to determine your knowledge
of hardiness and resiliency.

Please circle (T) if you think the statement is TRUE
and (F) if you think the statement is FALSE.

1. Resilient people are hardy . . . . T F

2. Resilient people never experience stress . . . . T F

3. Your level of resiliency can never be changed . . . . T F

4. Hardiness is the ability to stay well even with lots of stress . . . . T F

5. Hardiness allows you to view change as an opportunity . . . . T F

©2005 Wellness Reproductions & Publishing 1.800.669.9208

RESILIENT PERSONALITY INVENTORY

Name:

_____

_____

Gender:

_____

Date:

_____

Age:

_____

©2005 Wellness Reproductions & Publishing 1.800.669.9208

DIRECTIONS

The question has always arisen about why people react differently to stressful events. Some people are able to stay relatively stress-free during periods of a lot of personal change. This ability is referred to as resiliency. Resiliency is a pattern of qualities that determine who will succeed in surviving change and stress without illness. The Resilient Personality Inventory is designed to help you identify how hardy you are in times of transition.

This booklet contains 32 statements that are divided into four sections. Read each statement and decide how close the statement is with your beliefs about yourself and about the world.

> Circle 3 if the statement is – A Lot Like My Beliefs
>
> Circle 2 if the statement is – A Little Like My Beliefs
>
> Circle 1 if the statement is – Not Like My Beliefs

> 3 = A Lot Like My Beliefs   2 = A Little Like My Beliefs   1 = Not Like My Beliefs

It is natural for things to change   3 ② 1

In the above statement, the circled 2 means that the statement is a little like the beliefs of the test taker. Ignore the TOTAL lines below each section. They are for scoring purposes and will be used later.

> This is not a test. Since there are no right or wrong answers, do not spend too much time thinking about your answers. Be sure to respond to every statement.

Turn to the next page and begin.

©2005 Wellness Reproductions & Publishing 1.800.669.9208

RESILIENCY PERSONALITY INVENTORY

3 = A Lot Like My Beliefs	2 = A Little Like My Beliefs	1 = Not Like My Beliefs

I. CHALLENGE

It is natural for things to change.	3	2	1
Change is an opportunity for creativity.	3	2	1
I thrive under conditions of difficulty and adversity.	3	2	1
I can turn change into opportunity.	3	2	1
I am able to rise to the occasion in stressful situations.	3	2	1
I view stress as lessons to learn in life.	3	2	1
Stressful events are necessary for personal growth.	3	2	1
I view problems as challenges.	3	2	1
TOTAL = _____			

II. COMMITMENT

I find it easy to be contented in what I am doing.	3	2	1
I do what I love and love what I do.	3	2	1
I am rarely at a loss for things to do.	3	2	1
I am committed to my friends and family.	3	2	1
I always make maximum effort.	3	2	1
I am committed to life and to my interests.	3	2	1
I work because I enjoy it rather than feeling compelled.	3	2	1
I am committed to being successful at all I do.	3	2	1
TOTAL = _____			

Go on to the next page.

RESILIENCY PERSONALITY INVENTORY

3 = A Lot Like My Beliefs	2 = A Little Like My Beliefs	1 = Not Like My Beliefs

III. CONTROL

I believe I can influence events in my life.	3	2	1
I can influence my reactions to events in my life.	3	2	1
I think about how to turn difficult situations into opportunities.	3	2	1
I have a strong sense of initiative.	3	2	1
I rarely give up on a challenge.	3	2	1
I usually take positive action to reduce stress.	3	2	1
I can control negative thoughts during times of stress.	3	2	1
I react optimistically to transitions in my life.	3	2	1
TOTAL = _____			

IV. CREATIVITY

I am an intuitive thinker.	3	2	1
I often think imaginatively.	3	2	1
I tend to be very curious about people and things.	3	2	1
I have a positive vision of what is possible.	3	2	1
I have a childlike ability to amuse myself.	3	2	1
I have fun with activities and ideas.	3	2	1
I am playful and spontaneous.	3	2	1
I can visualize and see mental pictures.	3	2	1
TOTAL = _____			

Go to the scoring directions on the next page.

©2005 Wellness Reproductions & Publishing 1.800.669.9208

SCORING DIRECTIONS

People who are resilient do not become stressed under conditions of rapid and clustered change, and they actually thrive in the situation. A combination of attitudes is critical in determining whether people under stress get sick or not. The concept of resiliency involves a sense of challenge, commitment, control, and creativity. The Resilient Personality Inventory is designed to measure how resilient you are during times of change. Add the numbers you have circled for each of the four sections on the previous pages. Put that total on the line marked TOTAL at the end of each section.

Then, transfer your totals to the spaces below:

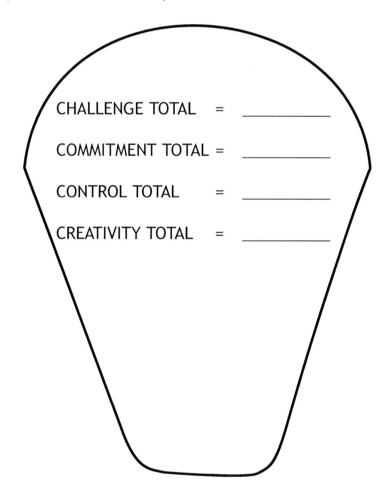

CHALLENGE TOTAL   =   _____

COMMITMENT TOTAL =   _____

CONTROL TOTAL   =   _____

CREATIVITY TOTAL   =   _____

©2005 Wellness Reproductions & Publishing 1.800.669.9208

PROFILE INTERPRETATION

As society continues moving at a faster pace, we live with more stress and thus are at a greater risk to become mentally or physically disabled. People with resilient personalities are able to give up distorted or obsolete ways of looking at issues important in their lives and adapt to change. In addition, they are able to integrate new perspectives and patterns of behavior in their approach to coping with stress. People with resilient personalities gain confidence as they experience success, are proud of their accomplishments, are aware of their passions, engage in self-examination, and are able to express their unique talents.

SCORES FROM 19 TO 24 IN ANY SINGLE AREA ARE HIGH and indicate that you have been able to develop hardiness in those areas.

SCORES FROM 14 TO 18 IN ANY SINGLE AREA ARE AVERAGE and indicate that you have been able to develop some hardiness in those areas, but still need some additional assistance.

SCORES FROM 8 AND 13 IN ANY SINGLE AREA ARE LOW and indicate that you need to take a more active role in developing hardiness in those areas.

In the areas in which you score in the "Low" or "Average" range, you should make efforts to increase your resiliency in those areas. Since this is not an easy thing to do, the following pages contain ideas and activities for you to complete in order to help you handle change with less stress. Read each description and then complete the exercises to improve your resiliency.

©2005 Wellness Reproductions & Publishing 1.800.669.9208

SCALE I – CHALLENGE

CHALLENGE is defined as the ability to view life changes and potentially stressful situations as opportunities rather than threats. Challenge relates to your ability to effectively manage stress. People who are resilient are able to perceive stressful situations as opportunities. They are able to positively view the challenges of a stressful situation and even look at it as a learning experience. They see themselves as having many different options in these types of situations.

In what ways is your life changing?

_____

_____

What problems are you currently experiencing?

_____

_____

How can you view these problems differently?

    As a challenge? _____

    As excitement? _____

    Finding some pleasure in it? _____

What major stress have you had in the last six months?

_____

_____

How have you handled the stress during this time?

_____

_____

Did you respond effectively?

_____

_____

How could you have handled the stress better?

_____

_____

SCALE II – COMMITMENT

COMMITMENT is defined as one's sense of involvement and meaning in what is occurring in life. People exhibiting resiliency feel a sense of commitment toward themselves, their relationships, work, hobbies, community, and spirituality, to name a few areas. They tend to give their full attention to interests in their lives. They have a pervasive sense of direction and they are committed to follow this path. People who are resilient work hard because they enjoy it, not because they feel compelled to do it. It is important that you explore the types of things that you enjoy doing and do well.

WHAT I DO WELL

List what you like to do, and do well, in the various roles you play:

_____

_____

In my role as a worker, I am good at:

_____

_____

In my role as a friend, I am good at:

_____

_____

In my role as a student, I am good at:

_____

_____

In my role as a parent, I am good at:

_____

_____

In my role as a child, I am good at:

_____

_____

In my role as a person who enjoys leisure, I am good at:

_____

_____

©2005 Wellness Reproductions & Publishing 1.800.669.9208

SCALE II – COMMITMENT (CONT'D)

MY SUCCESSES

From any roles you play, list what you are most proud of on the lines below:

ROLES	WHAT I AM PROUD OF

Turn to the next page and continue.

SCALE II – COMMITMENT (CONT'D)
MY DREAM JOB

The following questions will provide you with insights into your dream job:

What would you do during your perfect day?

_____

_____

If you could have any job, what would it be?

_____

_____

What were your childhood dreams and fantasies?

_____

_____

As a child, what did you love to do?

_____

_____

As an adult, what do you love to do?

_____

_____

SETTING GOALS

By making a strong commitment to your dreams, you create your own motivation, rather than relying on external circumstances to do so. Now you must set purposeful goals to help you maintain your motivation. Write a list of short-range goals that will act as stepping-stones to attaining each of your long-range goals.

Long-range goal #1 and short-range goals:

_____

_____

Long-range goal #2 and short-range goals:

_____

_____

Long-range goal #3 and short-range goals:

_____

©2005 Wellness Reproductions & Publishing 1.800.669.9208

SCALE III – CONTROL

CONTROL is defined as the belief that an individual has influence over his or her life. Resilient people are able to identify what they do and do not have control over. They tend to control their thoughts about the stress they are encountering, their feelings about the situation, how they behave, and their choices. It is the firm belief that they can influence how they will react and the willingness to act on that belief.

What types of activities can you successfully complete that will help you gain control in your life (e.g., paint your house, complete a project, etc.)?

_____

_____

_____

_____

Learning to relax is one way of controlling stress. What are some different ways that you can relax more?

_____

_____

_____

_____

List everything that is causing you stress:

_____

_____

_____

_____

_____

SCALE III — CONTROL (CONT'D)

THINGS I CAN CONTROL

Now take all of the stressors you listed on the page titled "SCALE III — CONTROL" and divide them into the following two categories:

WHAT I CAN CONTROL	WHAT I CANNOT CONTROL

Turn to the next page and continue.

©2005 Wellness Reproductions & Publishing 1.800.669.9208

SCALE III — CONTROL (CONT'D)

STRATEGIES for CONTROL

Now take all of the stressors you listed on the page titled "SCALE III — CONTROL" that you <u>can</u> control, and devise a strategy for doing so:

STRESSORS	STRATEGY FOR CONTROL

Turn to the next page and continue.

©2005 Wellness Reproductions & Publishing 1.800.669.9208

SCALE III — CONTROL (CONT'D)

STRATEGIES for OVERCOMING

Now take all of the stressors you listed on the page titled "SCALE III — CONTROL" that you <u>cannot</u> control, and devise a strategy to overcome the stress:

STRESSORS	STRATEGY FOR OVERCOMING

Turn to the next page and continue.

©2005 Wellness Reproductions & Publishing 1.800.669.9208

SCALE IV – CREATIVITY

People who are resilient see change as a stimulus for creativity. They are able to turn stressful situations and transitions into opportunities. Creativity can expand your awareness and open doors to new points of view. Resilient people are able to generate many points of view and new patterns, identify undetected relationships between ideas or events, and find unusual combinations for familiar elements.

Under what types of circumstances do you find your creative self awakening?

_____

_____

_____

What talents do you naturally have?

_____

_____

_____

Where and when do you create or want to create?

_____

_____

_____

What activates your creative energies?

_____

_____

_____

What drains your creative energies?

_____

_____

_____

©2005 Wellness Reproductions & Publishing 1.800.669.9208

SCALE IV — CREATIVITY (CONT'D)
IMAGINATION EXERCISES to BUILD CREATIVE THINKING

Here are thought-provoking questions that force you to engage in critical and creative thinking.

What if there were no televisions?

_____

_____

What if people were immortal?

_____

_____

Would you rather be a door or a window? Why?

_____

_____

Would you rather be a cat or a dog? Why?

_____

_____

What kind of car would you like to be? Why?

_____

_____

What would happen if people could fly?

_____

_____

If you had two heads on your shoulders, what would you do with them?

_____

_____

(Continued on next page)

©2005 Wellness Reproductions & Publishing 1.800.669.9208

SCALE IV – CREATIVITY (CONT'D)
IMAGINATION EXERCISES
to BUILD CREATIVE THINKING (CONT'D)

What if people could become invisible....what would happen?

_____

_____

What if you could read other people's thoughts?

_____

_____

If you could become any age again, what age would you want to be? Why?

_____

_____

What type of animal would you want to be? Why?

_____

_____

What kinds of things could you do if you were ten feet tall?

_____

_____

Would you rather be Batman, Superman, or Wonder Woman? Why?

_____

_____

What would happen if all people looked alike?

_____

_____

GROUP ACTIVITY

PREPARATION:

1 Prepare flipcharts and markers.

2 Write on the flipchart the words "Challenge," "Commitment," "Control," and "Creativity."

3 Give each group member a piece of paper and pen.

SESSION:

1 Ask group members to think about words that describe each of the four words written on the flipchart. (1 minute)

2 Ask group members, "What are several words that mean the same thing as Challenge?" and write this question on the flipchart. Give group members a few minutes to jot down ideas. Share and write all responses on the flipchart. (3 minutes)

3 Ask group members, "What are several words that mean the same thing as Commitment?" and write this question on the flipchart. Give group members a few minutes to jot down ideas. Share and write all responses on the flipchart. (3 minutes)

4 Ask group members, "What are several words that mean the same thing as Control?" and write this question on the flipchart. Give group members a few minutes to jot down ideas. Share and write all responses on the flipchart. (3 minutes)

5 Ask group members, "What are several words that mean the same thing as Creativity?" and write this question on the flipchart. Give group members a few minutes to jot down ideas. Share and write all responses on the flipchart. (3 minutes)

6 Break group participants into smaller groups based on their personality type. Have each group identify the major advantages and disadvantages of their personality type. Then have them identify the major advantages and disadvantages of the other personality types. (10 minutes)

Reconvene in larger group and share experiences. (10 minutes)

7 Process by asking one or more of the following questions: (5 minutes)

8
- What did you learn about your own resiliency personality type?

- What was most effective about each type of resiliency personality?

- What was least effective about each of the resiliency personality types?

©2005 Wellness Reproductions & Publishing 1.800.669.9208

PEOPLE with HARDINESS:

- work hard because they enjoy it.

- react to change optimistically.

- take positive action in life.

- view stress as interesting.

- see stress as important.

- see stress as a potential for growth.

- believe they can influence stressful events.

- consider stress to be a natural part of life.

- see stress as an opportunity for creativity.

PERSONAL INSIGHTS:

- _____

- _____

- _____

CHARACTERISTICS
of HARDINESS

- CHALLENGE — The ability to thrive under conditions of challenge and difficulty

- COMMITMENT — The ability to commit to what you love and give it your very best effort

- CONTROL — The ability to influence events and your reactions to the events

- CREATIVITY — The ability to see stress and change as opportunities for creative expression

PERSONAL INSIGHTS:

- _____

- _____

- _____

©2005 Wellness Reproductions & Publishing 1.800.669.9208

EFFECTS of
HARDINESS

- Greater self-esteem

- More energy when you need it

- Higher quality of life

- Greater optimism

- Fewer feelings of sadness and depression

- Better general health

- Greater sense of meaning

- Greater sense of life direction and purpose

- Fewer days absent from work / school

PERSONAL INSIGHTS:

- _____

- _____

- _____

©2005 Wellness Reproductions & Publishing 1.800.669.9208

TIME-MANAGEMENT MODULE

The Time-Management Scale helps people identify strengths and weaknesses in managing time in their lives and learn more effective methods of time management.

INDEX

Answers to the pre- and post-test — page 84:	
1. Time urgency is one of the biggest problems in the United States	True
2. Procrastination often occurs because of perfectionism	True
3. Having too many obligations is a time-management problem	True
4. Time management has little to do with stress	False
5. The management of time is vital to health and wellness	True

©2005 Wellness Reproductions & Publishing 1.800.669.9208

TIME-MANAGEMENT SCALE

PRE-and POST-TEST

NAME: _____ DATE: _____

The following true-or-false questions
are designed to determine your knowledge
of time management and how time management
affects your overall sense of wellness.

Please circle (T) if you think the statement is **TRUE**
and (F) if you think the statement is **FALSE.**

---

1. Time urgency is one of the biggest problems in the United States . . . . T   F

2. Procrastination often occurs because of perfectionism . . . . T   F

3. Having too many obligations is a time-management problem . . . . T   F

4. Time management has little to do with stress . . . . T   F

5. The management of time is vital to health and wellness . . . . T   F

©2005 Wellness Reproductions & Publishing 1.800.669.9208

TIME-MANAGEMENT
SCALE

Name:

_____

_____

Gender:

_____

Date:

_____

Age:

_____

©2005 Wellness Reproductions & Publishing 1.800.669.9208

DIRECTIONS

Time means many things to different people. For some people, time brings pleasure, satisfaction, and challenge. For other people, time brings anxiety, stress, exhaustion, and confusion. One of the leading causes of stress is that we often have too much to do and not enough time to do all that we want to. In this fast-paced society, learning how to manage your time can help you to alleviate stress and reduce anxiety in your life.

The Time-Management Scale (TMS) can help you identify whether you are managing time in your life or if it is managing you. People with good time-management skills are better prepared to organize their life and their work, minimize the stress in their life, maximize the results of goals they set for themselves, and enhance how they relate to time.

This assessment contains 40 statements. Read each of the statements and decide if the statement is true or false. If it is true, circle the word "True" next to the statement. If the statement is false, circle the word "False" next to the statement. Ignore the letters after the True and False choices. They are for scoring purposes and will be used later. Do all 40 items before going back to score the TMS.

In the following example, the circled False indicates that the item is false for the person completing the TMS:

1.   I often put off calling people I don't like   True   (A)   (False) (B)   Score _____

This is not a test. Since there are no right or wrong answers, do not spend too much time thinking about your answers. Be sure to respond to every statement.

Turn to the next page and begin.

©2005 Wellness Reproductions & Publishing 1.800.669.9208

TIME-MANAGEMENT SCALE

1. I often put off calling people I don't like.	True (A)	False (B)	Score _____
2. I spend most of my time working and being productive.	True (A)	False (B)	Score _____
3. I have plenty of time for hobbies or leisure activities.	True (B)	False (A)	Score _____
4. I often blame other people for keeping me so busy.	True (A)	False (B)	Score _____
5. I complete most projects at the last minute.	True (A)	False (B)	Score _____
6. Others cannot do my work because it will not meet my standards.	True (A)	False (B)	Score _____
7. I am often too busy to enjoy life.	True (A)	False (B)	Score _____
8. I often do things so that other people do not disapprove of me.	True (A)	False (B)	Score _____
9. I take pride in the fact that I usually put things off till the last minute.	True (A)	False (B)	Score _____
10. I rarely get upset when a task is incomplete.	True (B)	False (A)	Score _____
11. I make time to enjoy healthy pleasures in my life.	True (B)	False (A)	Score _____
12. I take on more commitments than I have time for.	True (A)	False (B)	Score _____
13. I rarely take risks because I am afraid of making mistakes.	True (A)	False (B)	Score _____
14. I always seem to be in a hurry.	True (A)	False (B)	Score _____
15. I have plenty of time to spend with my friends.	True (B)	False (A)	Score _____
16. I always feel like I am rushing from one thing to another.	True (A)	False (B)	Score _____
17. Because I am afraid of failing, I often put things off.	True (A)	False (B)	Score _____
18. I feel like I must be all things to all people.	True (A)	False (B)	Score _____
19. I am able to balance work, school, and leisure.	True (B)	False (A)	Score _____
20. I find myself doing things I do not want to do.	True (A)	False (B)	Score _____

Turn to the next page and continue.

©2005 Wellness Reproductions & Publishing 1.800.669.9208

TIME-MANAGEMENT SCALE

21. I wait until it is absolutely necessary to see a doctor or dentist.	True (A)	False (B)	Score _____
22. I am competitive and always have to win.	True (A)	False (B)	Score _____
23. I experience the beauty in everyday life.	True (B)	False (A)	Score _____
24. I say "no" if a commitment will take time away from my personal time.	True (B)	False (A)	Score _____
25. I often postpone appointments or meetings.	True (A)	False (B)	Score _____
26. I rarely try to do several things at the same time.	True (B)	False (A)	Score _____
27. I make time for intimate relationships.	True (B)	False (A)	Score _____
28. I have realistic expectations of myself.	True (B)	False (A)	Score _____
29. I put off tasks that are not clearly defined or planned.	True (A)	False (B)	Score _____
30. I must always get the most done in the least amount of time.	True (A)	False (B)	Score _____
31. I enjoy the time when I am not working.	True (B)	False (A)	Score _____
32. I often feel obligated to do many things at one time.	True (A)	False (B)	Score _____
33. I complete tasks quickly even if they are unpleasant.	True (B)	False (A)	Score _____
34. The only important thing in life is "to get ahead."	True (A)	False (B)	Score _____
35. I do not have trouble relaxing on the weekends.	True (B)	False (A)	Score _____
36. I have trouble saying "no" to new opportunities even if they overload me.	True (A)	False (B)	Score _____
37. There is a right answer and I will wait till I find it.	True (A)	False (B)	Score _____
38. I feel driven to do and get more money than other people.	True (A)	False (B)	Score _____
39. I enjoy being with people, but I also like being by myself.	True (B)	False (A)	Score _____
40. I often say "yes' when I mean "no."	True (A)	False (B)	Score _____

Go to the scoring directions on the next page.

©2005 Wellness Reproductions & Publishing 1.800.669.9208

SCORING

The Time-Management Scale (TMS) is designed to help you to identify your time-management strengths and weaknesses. The TMS will help assist you in the identification of areas in which you might be able to manage your time better. To score the TMS, you need to determine your scores on each of the individual scales and also for the overall TIME-MANAGEMENT TOTAL. Four scales have been identified that indicate how well you are managing time in your life. These areas include: Procrastination, Chronic Urgency, Inadequate Time, and Unwanted Obligations. These four areas make up the scales for the TMS.

TO SCORE THE TMS: Look at the 40 items you just completed. Now you need to focus on the "A" and "B" after each choice rather than the "True" or "False." In the space marked "Score" for each item, award yourself ONE (1) point for every answer you circled with a "B" next to it and ZERO (0) points for every answer you circled with an "A" next to it.

Use the spaces below to transfer your scores to each of the scales below.

PROCRASTINATION SCALE: # 1_____, # 5_____, # 9_____, # 13_____, # 17_____,
21_____, # 25_____, # 29_____, # 33_____, # 37_____ = _____

CHRONIC URGENCY SCALE: # 2_____, # 6_____, # 10_____, # 14_____, # 18_____,
22_____, # 26_____, # 30_____, # 34_____, # 38_____ = _____

INADEQUATE TIME SCALE: # 3_____, # 7_____, # 11_____, # 15_____, # 19_____,
23_____, # 27_____, # 31_____, # 35_____, # 39_____ = _____

UNWANTED OBLIGATIONS SCALE: # 4_____, # 8_____, # 12_____, # 16_____, # 20_____,
24_____, # 28_____, # 32_____, # 36_____, # 40_____ = _____

Then, write the individual totals of the individual scales and add them all together to get a Total and write that number in the TIME-MANAGEMENT TOTAL blank below:

Procrastination Scale: _____

Chronic Urgency Scale: _____

Inadequate Time Scale: _____

Unwanted Obligations Scale: _____

TIME-MANAGEMENT TOTAL _____

Turn to the next page to interpret your scores.

©2005 Wellness Reproductions & Publishing 1.800.669.9208

PROFILE INTERPRETATION

SCORES FROM 0 TO 3 ON THE INDIVIDUAL SCALES, AND A TOTAL SCORE FROM 0 TO 13 ARE LOW and may indicate that you do not manage your time well. You probably put projects off till the last minute because you are too busy. You tend to always seem to be in a hurry and are not able to balance work, school, and leisure. People with limited time-management skills always feel they must be busy. You take on too many commitments and then are forced to do many different things at the same time. You feel driven and work hard to fulfill your obligations. Unfortunately, this leaves little time for leisure, friends, and family.

SCORES FROM 4 TO 6 ON THE INDIVIDUAL SCALES, AND A TOTAL SCORE FROM 14 TO 26 ARE AVERAGE and may indicate that you have time-management skills similar to most other people. Average scores suggest that you tend to control time, but need to work to be a better time manager.

SCORES FROM 7 TO 10 ON THE INDIVIDUAL SCALES, AND A TOTAL SCORE FROM 27 TO 40 ARE HIGH and may indicate that you are an effective time manager. You tend to take the time to enjoy life and are able to effectively balance work, school, and leisure. You rarely procrastinate in completing projects and are able to tell people "no" if you do not want additional obligations. You are rarely in a hurry and have plenty of time for hobbies and leisure activities. You make time for all of the important things in life and do not feel you have to be productive every moment. You tend to do one thing at a time and are not afraid to delegate work to other people and trust that the work will get done.

The higher your score on the TMS, the better your time-management scores are. In the areas in which you score in the "Low" or "Average" ranges, make efforts to enhance your time-management skills. The exercises and activities that follow are designed to help you to increase your time-management skills. Even if you scored in the high range on all four scales, a relatively lower score in one test might be an area of potential growth. You may choose to do all the exercises and activities in that area.

©2005 Wellness Reproductions & Publishing 1.800.669.9208

MANAGING PROCRASTINATING BEHAVIOR:

● **STOP PROCRASTINATING**
What do you find yourself putting off till later?

_____

_____

Why do you put them off till later?

_____

_____

● **MONITOR NEGATIVE SELF-TALK**
What negative words do you find that "little voice inside your head" saying to you?

_____

_____

● **REPLACE "SHOULDS" WITH "OUGHTS"**
What do you feel obligated to do, or think that you should always do?

_____

_____

Now make each of the above shoulds into oughts.

_____

_____

● **STOP WORRYING ABOUT HOW OTHERS VIEW YOU**
What do you worry about in trying to impress others?

_____

_____

What do you think others say about you?

_____

_____

● **STOP OVERREACTING TO MISTAKES**

(Continued on next page.)

MANAGING PROCRASTINATING BEHAVIOR (CONT'D)

List possible mistakes that you have made and list what is the worst that could happen:

MISTAKES	WHAT IS THE WORST THAT COULD HAPPEN?

©2005 Wellness Reproductions & Publishing 1.800.669.9208

MANAGING CHRONIC URGENCY

● **FIND A HOBBY**

Activities I enjoy that are not work-related:

_____

_____

Activities I can do that are not competitive in nature:

_____

_____

I deny myself these pleasures because:

_____

_____

● **DELEGATE RESPONSIBILITIES**

I do these things that do not require my personal attention:

_____

_____

I could delegate these things to:

_____

_____

● **MONITOR NEGATIVE SELF-TALK**

When I start to feel driven to accomplish things, I say to myself:

_____

_____

Typical "I should" thoughts or "you should" thoughts are:

_____

_____

©2005 Wellness Reproductions & Publishing 1.800.669.9208

MANAGING CHRONIC URGENCY (CONT'D)

● ACTIVATE YOUR RIGHT-BRAIN
I enjoy, or could enjoy, this type of literature and music, without being competitive or obsessed with it:

_____

_____

I could engage in these types of artistic activities solely for the enjoyment of doing them:

_____

_____

● LOOK AT PREVIOUS RELAXATION "SUCCESSES"
I have enjoyed these types of relaxing activities in the past:

_____

_____

● SCHEDULE TIME EACH DAY TO REST AND RELAX
List some things you could do each day to slow down or stop your achieving ways:

_____

_____

I can begin using these types of stress-reducing techniques to help me relax:
(meditation, walking, jogging, deep breathing, hobbies)

_____

_____

● LEARN TO DO THINGS JUST FOR THE FUN OF IT
What types of activities do you want to do simply because they are fun and not because they will help your career?

_____

_____

©2005 Wellness Reproductions & Publishing 1.800.669.9208

MANAGING INADEQUATE TIME

● DETERMINE HOW YOU ARE SPENDING YOUR TIME
Write down information about what you do during a typical day:

_____

_____

What changes could you make to have more free time for yourself?

_____

_____

● CONTINUE TO SPEND TIME BY YOURSELF AS WELL AS WITH OTHERS
When, during the day, could you find time to relax or meditate?
What is stopping you from using that time to reenergize yourself?

_____

_____

● DETERMINE HOW YOUR FAMILY IS AFFECTING YOUR USE OF TIME
How has your family, upbringing, or ethnic background affected your sense of time?

_____

_____

What could you block out and not do, to have more time by yourself?

_____

_____

How can you spend more time with other people?

_____

_____

● CONTINUE TO ENGAGE IN PLEASURABLE LEISURE ACTIVITIES
What are some leisure activities you can engage in to have time by yourself?

_____

_____

MANAGING INADEQUATE TIME (CONT'D)

Following is a schedule of the pleasurable activities I want to engage in:

PLEASURABLE ACTIVITIES	WHEN I WILL DO THEM EACH DAY / WEEK

©2005 Wellness Reproductions & Publishing 1.800.669.9208

MANAGING UNWANTED OBLIGATIONS

DEFINE ROLE EXPECTATIONS

What is expected of you by yourself or by others that is unrealistic?

WHERE	UNREALISTIC EXPECTATIONS
At Home	
At Work	
With Friends	
At School	
In the Community	

EXERCISE FOR STRESS REDUCTION

SAY "NO" TO OTHERS IF YOU MEAN NO

What types of situations do you find yourself saying "yes" when you mean "no?"

_____

_____

_____

Why do you find yourself saying "yes" in these situations?

_____

_____

_____

To whom do you say "yes" when you mean "no?"

_____

_____

_____

To whom do you need to start saying "no" more often?

_____

_____

_____

What fears do you have about being more assertive?

_____

_____

_____

What types of commitments and obligations do you take on that you do not need to?

_____

_____

©2005 Wellness Reproductions & Publishing 1.800.669.9208

STRESS REDUCTION (CONT'D)

BE ASSERTIVE WHEN YOU NEED TO BE

List a situation in which you find yourself not being as assertive as you could be:

ASSERTIVE STEPS:	EXAMPLE:	NOW YOU TRY IT:
What are your rights? What do you want and need?	I want more time to do yoga, but I'm so busy with my family obligations that I don't have the time.	
Plan a time to discuss your problem.	Tuesday night after dinner.	
Define the problem	I need more time do some things that are fun and relaxing for me, but I am too busy working and doing housework to find the time.	
Describe the problem using "I" Messages	I feel exhausted and disappointed that you will not chip in and do more around the house.	
Express your needs	I need you to help with household chores like doing the dishes, grocery shopping, or taking care of the children.	
Express the positive outcome	I will have some free time by myself to do some things that I enjoy, like yoga.	

STRESS REDUCTION (CONT'D)

SET MORE REALISTIC AND ACHIEVABLE GOALS

What would you like to accomplish within the next 5 years? Is this realistic?

_____

_____

_____

_____

_____

What would you like to accomplish within the next 3 years? Is this realistic?

_____

_____

_____

_____

_____

What would you like to accomplish within the next year? Is this realistic?

_____

_____

_____

_____

_____

©2005 Wellness Reproductions & Publishing 1.800.669.9208

TIME-MANAGEMENT EXERCISE

Identify a major time-management problem that you have been involved in during the past year. This problem could have been when you procrastinated in doing something, felt tired from always being in a hurry, did not have enough time to do all you wanted to do, or when you had too many obligations to meet.

Time-Management Situation: _____

1. What caused the time-management problem?

2. How could you have avoided the problem?

3. What was the result from this problem?

4. What strategies would you now use to avoid this same type of problem?

©2005 Wellness Reproductions & Publishing 1.800.669.9208

GROUP ACTIVITY

PREPARATION:

1 Prepare flipcharts and markers.

2 Write on the flipchart the words "Procrastination," "Chronic Urgency," "Inadequate Time," and "Unwanted Obligations."

3 Give each group member a piece of paper and pen.

SESSION:

1 Discuss the definitions and causes of the four types of time-management problems. (5 minutes)

2 Ask group members, "Explain and describe how you think people with procrastination time-management problems live their lives," and write this on the flipchart. Give group members a few minutes to jot down ideas. Share and write all responses on

3 the flipchart. (3 minutes)

Ask group members, "Explain and describe how you think people with chronic urgency time-management problems live their lives" and write this on the flipchart. Give group members a few minutes to jot down ideas. Share and write all responses on the flipchart. (3 minutes)

4 Ask group members, "Explain and describe how you think people with time-inadequacy time-management problems live their lives" and write this on the flip chart. Give group members a few minutes to jot down ideas. Share and write all responses on

5 the flip chart. (3 minutes)

Ask group members, "Explain and describe how you think people with unwanted obligations time-management problems live their lives" and write this on the flipchart. Give group members a few minutes to jot down ideas. Share and write all responses

6 on the flipchart. (3 minutes)

Divide the group into smaller groups based on their primary time-management problem. Have the members of each group brainstorm ways in which they will work to overcome their time-management problems. Have one person in the group write

7 these answers down on paper to share with the larger group. (10 minutes)

8 Reconvene in larger group and share experiences and solutions to each group's time-management problems. (10 minutes)

Ask group members to share personal insights gained from this activity. (10 minutes)

©2005 Wellness Reproductions & Publishing 1.800.669.9208

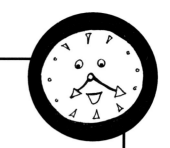

HOW TO MANAGE YOUR TIME BETTER?

● Identify realistic long- and short-term goals.

● Delegate work whenever possible.

● Protect your personal time and space.

● Avoid procrastinating.

● Make time for healthy pleasures.

● Waste less time.

● Say "no" when you do not want to do something.

● Avoid doing more than one thing at a time.

PERSONAL INSIGHTS:

● _____

● _____

● _____

©2005 Wellness Reproductions & Publishing 1.800.669.9208

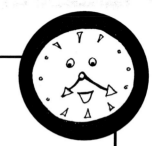

FOUR TIME-MANAGEMENT PROBLEMS

● Procrastination — Putting off things that you know you do not need to do or want to do.

● Chronic Urgency — Feeling rushed, harried, and hassled in keeping up the demands at work, school, and home.

● Inadequate Time — Feeling like there is not enough time in the day to do all you have to do and still have time for fun and relaxation.

● Unwanted Obligation — Having trouble saying "no" to other people so that you have more obligations than you have time to complete.

PERSONAL INSIGHTS:

● _____

● _____

● _____

©2005 Wellness Reproductions & Publishing 1.800.669.9208

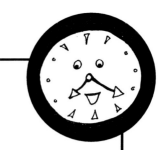

IRRATIONAL BELIEFS ABOUT TIME

● I must always be working on something.

● I cannot delegate work because it will not be done perfectly.

● If it's not done right, it's not worth doing at all.

● I have no control over the constant overload in my life.

● All people feel as rushed as I do.

● I must always be in a hurry to get everything done.

● I must be all things to all people.

● If I say "no" to someone asking me to do something I don't want to do, I'm a bad person.

● I must always be doing several things at once.

PERSONAL INSIGHTS:

● _____

● _____

● _____

NOTES

©2005 Wellness Reproductions & Publishing 1.800.669.9208